S0-BRO-978

713

244-3 411-5

Best wishes
Margaret Denny Dixon

Given to the
Roanoke Public Library
by
Esther Coulbourn Dance
regent for
Margaret Lynn Lewis Chapter
Daughters of the American
1954   Revolution

The Princess
of the
Old Dominion

A Historical Novel of the
First Virginia Colony by

MARGARET DENNY DIXON

EXPOSITION PRESS · NEW YORK

FIRST EDITION

All rights reserved including the right of
reproduction in whole or in part in any form
Copyright, 1953, by Margaret Denny Dixon
Published by the Exposition Press Inc.
386 Fourth Avenue, New York 16, N.Y.
Designed by Morry M. Gropper
Manufactured in the United States of America
Consolidated Book Producers, Inc.
Library of Congress catalog card number: 53-6713

134331

Cap. 5 √Ref

To my oldest grandchildren,
Mimi, Margaret, Ted and John,
who are also grandchildren of
the Princess of the Old Dominion

Acknowledgments

Special thanks are due the following persons for their kindness in reading the manuscript of this book and checking it for historical accuracy:

Dr. Arthur Pierce Middleton, Director of Research and Archives of Colonial Williamsburg, who gave helpful information about the celebration of the first Communion service.

Miss Ellen M. Bagby, Chairman of the Jamestown Committee of the Association for the Preservation of Virginia Antiquities.

Dr. G. MacLaren Brydon, Historiographer of the Episcopal Diocese of Virginia.

Mrs. Robert N. Murphy, Deputy Governor of the Virginia Society of Mayflower Descendants.

MARGARET DENNY DIXON

Contents

THE PRINCESS OF THE OLD DOMINION

CHAPTER I

John Smith of Virginia

In early spring of the year 1607, a fleet of three small vessels slowly crept through the two capes that mark the entrance to Chesapeake Bay. Even there they did not obtain rest from the raging waves, and during a long, wild night they struggled against destruction. With the first gray light in the east the storm ceased and the rising sun revealed a bright, beautiful coast. The party made haste to land and knelt upon the sand while a prayer was offered.

The vessels—the *Sarah Constant,* the *Good Speed* and the *Discovery*—had been sent to Virginia by the Virginia Company of London and were under the command of Captain Christopher Newport. For four months they had struggled with a winter sea, and now, just as the earth was growing green, they were approaching Virginia. It had been a stormy voyage in more ways than one. The money for the enterprise had been furnished by the Virginia Company of London. The local government was to be in the hands of a Council of seven men appointed by the Council of Virginia, which had placed the names of members of the local Council in a box that was not to be opened till the colonists landed in Virginia. While the waves were endeavoring to tear the ships to pieces, the men themselves, by internal jealousies, were laying the foundation for future trouble. Long before the vessels sighted land, two of the number—John Smith and Jehu Robinson—were arrested on the charge that they were scheming to make themselves kings of Virginia.

It was April when the tired voyagers first touched the land that was to be the future home of a few and the grave of many of their number. In order to end the suspense that was causing unrest and jealousy, Master Hunt, the godly chaplain of the colony, advised that the box containing the names of the councilors be opened at once. The whole company, save the two men under arrest, was drawn up on the deck while Master Hunt slowly and clearly called the names of the seven men who were to control the destiny of the colony for the next year. The name of Bartholomew Gosnold brought sounds of approval, for he had the respect of all. At the reading of the second name, that of John Smith, a chorus of voices was heard; many shouted approval and as many others voiced dissent.

Master Hunt held up his hand. "We have no say in the matter, my friends. The Council for Virginia has made the choice, and we must bide by it for a year."

No special pleasure or displeasure was expressed as the other five names were read: Edward Maria Wingfield, Captain Christopher Newport, John Ratcliff, John Martin and George Kendall. The men were to elect a president from among their number. They retired to the cabin of the ship to complete their organization in private. The door had scarcely shut when Kendall burst out, "I object to giving a seat to John Smith. I have proof that he and his confederates plotted to murder the members of the Council as soon as the names were announced, and to usurp the government for themselves."

"Hold!" shouted Master Gosnold. "You made that charge while we bided at the Canaries. Master Hunt questioned your witnesses and they did not bear you out. Is it not enough that you caused Captain Smith to be confined to the hold for the rest of the voyage, without continuing the complaint here in this new land? We need peace and harmony if our new colony is to succeed."

"Master Gosnold speaks truly, gentlemen," said Captain Newport. "Let us proceed with the election of our president. Our charter from the Company allows trial by jury. May we not settle the matter of Captain Smith as Englishmen should?"

After Master Wingfield had been elected president, the Council settled down to a discussion of the instructions of the Company, enclosed in the box. They enjoined special care in the location of the colony. Because the colonists feared an attack from Spain, they did not choose a landing place near the ocean. They decided that on the next day they would take from the hold of one of the vessels a shallop that had been shipped in sections and could easily be fitted together, since this little craft could go more swiftly than the heavier vessels. Captain Newport was to have charge of the trip of investigation.

Again Kendall spoke. "Why keep Captain Smith confined in idleness? Let him go with Captain Newport, who will be able to guard him. If he remains here, he would likely spread more mischief."

Captain Newport looked scornfully at Kendall. "I shall be glad to have Captain Smith as part of my company. He is a man of energy and judgment and will do his share of any hard work."

For seventeen days they went slowly up the broad river they called the James in honor of their king, examining each bank. What they found delighted them. Many smaller rivers and streams flowed into the large one. Spring flowers were blooming everywhere. There were forests of familiar trees—cedar, cypress, beech, walnut—and others that were unknown to them. Grapevines hung from the trees. Tiny green strawberry plants were pushing through the covering of winter leaves. During the day they fished from the boat, scorning to take anything smaller than a sturgeon. In the evening they landed to cook their supper. It was at these times that the cautious scouts saw bears, foxes, otters, beavers and muskrats as well as other strange beasts.

At first they saw no Indians. One day, when they were about eight miles inland, they came upon a fire on which oysters were roasting, and they ate them with gusty enjoyment. Another day they found a canoe, forty feet long, made out of the trunk of a tree in which was a great store of oysters, some of them containing pearls. When the savages finally appeared, they showed themselves to be friendly and were delighted with the trinkets given to them.

At last, some thirty miles from the mouth of the river, they saw a low peninsula. They discovered that the ships could anchor close to shore, and chose to land here rather than on the mainland, where the ships would have to anchor some distance out in the river. The site proved to be an unfortunate selection, for the peninsula was marshy and much of it was under water at high tide. But here was founded Jamestown, the first permanent English settlement in America—an augury of what we see today.

As soon as they landed, after Master Hunt had prayed, their first act was formally to swear in the Council and to declare Wingfield president. Yielding to Master Hunt's persuasion, Smith did not then insist on taking his place on the Council.

Since the vessels would soon return to England, depriving the colonists of shelter, all, even some of the gentlemen, set about the labor of preparing shelter on land. So as to have a place for morning and evening prayer, an awning to shelter them from sun and rain was contrived by hanging a sail between three or four trees. The pulpit was a bar of wood nailed between two adjacent trees. The seats were unhewn trees, which served till planks could be cut. Wingfield suggested to Master Hunt that Holy Communion be celebrated the following Sunday. His face clouded with anger at the clergyman's reply: "I cannot suffer my flock to be partakers at the Lord's table till I am assured all are reconciled to each other."

"Are you thinking of Captain Smith?"

"Yea. Are you sure 'tis not malice and jealousy that is depriving him of his rightful place on the Council?"

With an effort Wingfield forced himself to adopt a more conciliatory tone of voice. "He will not trouble us long, since he is to return to England with Captain Newport to be judged by the Company."

"But mayhap he will refuse to go and will demand that he be tried here in Virginia."

"Master Hunt, I beg you to use your best endeavors to persuade Captain Smith to return to England. If we are forced to particularize his designs, it will make him so odious to his fellow colonists as to endanger his life. His reputation will be utterly overthrown."

"He hath an Englishman's right to a jury trial at the place where he is accused of crime."

Wingfield turned impatiently and strode off without mentioning again the matter of the Communion.

Meanwhile the work on the settlement was going forward. Out of trees that were being cut down to make space for pitching tents and planting gardens, clapboards were being cut with which to relade the ships on their return. Boughs of trees were piled behind the clearing, in the form of a half-moon, as their only fortification. Even the precaution of setting a guard was relaxed by Wingfield's order, since the Indians appeared friendly. Indeed, most of the arms were still in packing cases.

Captain Newport wished to take back to the London Company a full report of the country, so while work at Jamestown was proceeding, he continued his trip up the river, taking Captain Smith with him. They discovered a large Indian village called Powhatan. A mile above this village the river was no longer navigable, on account of rocks and small islands. There, on an abrupt hill overlooking the river, a cross similar to the one they had placed at Cape Henry two months earlier was planted and King James was proclaimed sovereign of the land.

A sorry sight greeted them on their return to Jamestown. When the Indians saw growing crops, they realized that the colonists had come to stay, so they set out to capture the town. The unarmed men were widely scattered at their work, and before they could gather together for defense, seventeen men were wounded and one boy was slain. At this critical moment a sailor on one of the vessels fired a cannon. His aim was poor and the ball struck a tree, but the falling branches and the noise so frightened the Indians that they fled in terror. After this, the Council decided to enclose the little settlement within a palisade. Since the sail-awning was not satisfactory for morning and evening prayers and the two Sunday services, a rude little church was one of the first buildings erected. It was an oblong structure, set upon cratches and covered with rafts, sedge and earth.

Again the matter of Holy Communion was brought up, this time by Captain Newport.

The gentle clergyman was deeply troubled. "Over and over in daily prayers and Sunday services I have mentioned brotherly love. I cannot administer the Sacrament to a flock in dissension."

"It has been nearly six months since we left England. My sailors should be blessed by the Sacrament ere they start the long voyage home."

"I know. I know," Master Hunt sadly replied. "Why cannot I lead them to realize that the welfare of our little colony depends on our union? We are in an unknown land, exposed to attacks of hostile natives, and we need the strength of brotherly love. President Wingfield is insisting that Captain Smith return to England; and rightly, he is refusing to go. He must not leave. We need his wisdom and strength. But if he remains and strife continues . . ."

Captain Newport interrupted him. "If I could persuade Wingfield to drop this scheme and allow a trial with a jury of men not on the Council, would that satisfy you?"

"So all agree to abide by the result and restore peace, my scruples will be removed."

Captain Newport insisted on an immediate trial, as the time of his departure was near. The result left a black spot on the reputation of the Council. The prosecution was conducted by George Kendall, assisted by a lawyer named Archer. The testimony of their own witnesses was proven false and the jury allowed Smith damages from Kendall and Wingfield.

With peace outwardly restored and Captain Smith admitted to the Council, Master Hunt, at the evening prayer, gave this timely exhortation: "The way to prosper and achieve good success is to make ourselves all of one mind for the good of our country and of ourselves. Every plantation which our Heavenly Father hath not planted shall be rooted out."

The next day, June 21, the third Sunday after Trinity, all received Communion. The vessels which had brought them over were to start their homeward journey the next day, and the handful of colonists would be left in the wilderness. Good Master Hunt's voice was husky with earnestness as he prayed that they should "by God's mighty aid, be defended and comforted in all dangers and adversities."

CHAPTER II

Disaster Strikes the Colony

When Captain Newport sailed back to England, he left at Jamestown one hundred and four men. A fearful summer followed. Newport had not left much food. The unexpectedly long voyage over had depleted the supply greatly, and naturally, he had taken with him enough to feed his men on the return trip. Over half the colonists were gentlemen, who expected to find food growing wild or to have it supplied to them. After they had assured themselves of some kind of permanent shelter, they were not disposed to do any further work.

When Cape Merchant Thomas Studley went to the storehouse to take an account of what Newport had left, he was surprised to find that President Wingfield had a key and was even then helping himself to some supplies. "I was but getting a bit of pork and other things from my private stock for my sick servant," he offered by way of explanation.

Studley hesitated to rebuke the president, but he reported the occurrence to Master Gosnold. "And since I was there yesterday, the supply of oatmeal hath greatly lessened. And the store of sack and brandy is all gone."

"I care not for the oatmeal," grumbled Ratcliffe, who had joined them. " 'Tis that coop of chickens he guards so carefully behind his house. Why could he not share his eggs with his sick servant?"

"The chickens are his own. We had done better had each brought a few hens for himself," replied Gosnold.

Meanwhile most of the colonists were eating from the common kettle, into which was put a daily allowance for each man of a half pint of wheat and as much barley, which was boiled in water. "The gentles will continue to go hungry an they do nothing to help themselves," whispered one laborer to another. "So long as my secret snare yields a young rabbit once in a while, I do not go hungry. 'Tis the water that sickens me. At high tide 'tis salt and at low 'tis full of slime and muck. We had done better to have settled at the place downstream that Master Gosnold and Captain Archer favored, even if the ships must needs anchor out in the river. We could have dug a well there."

"I can stomach the victuals and the water," replied the other. " 'Tis the cursed insects. All day and all night they sing and then they sting. See how I have clawed my flesh. I get relief only by sitting on the windward side of a fire, and in this heat that cannot be borne for long."

July dragged on. The sun shone mercilessly day after day, while the parched colonists scanned the brassy sky, hoping for rain. What they received came in the form of fierce thunder storms that beat through the flimsy roofs and sides of their houses.

Resentment against Wingfield grew. The Council tried to blame Studley for the small amount of food in the storehouse, but he defended himself hotly. "We left England in winter with victuals enow for two months at sea. We were supposed to have the advantage of spring in which to work. We were at sea for five months and lost the opportunity of the time and season to plant. The few seeds we did sow are yielding poorly on account of the sun and the lack of rain. What little has ripened is eaten at once, with no thought of winter. I do not rightly know what Captain Newport left us, but I do know our small store of oil and vinegar hath disappeared." He added sullenly, "Others have a key to the storehouse also."

"At least our president does not lessen the supply in the common store by eating from it himself," whispered Martin to Ratcliffe.

"Why should any man in his senses do so, had he aught else to eat? Didst hear that someone broke into his chest and found sweetmeats and other tidbits? Wingfield is shamed to complain of their loss."

Many of the men complained of illness in July, and in August the heavy blow fell. Thomas Wotten, the chirurgeon general, reported that there was a dangerous case of bloody flux. On the sixth of the month the sick man died. The rest of the month was a nightmare. The Indians continued to prowl around the palisade to pick off stragglers. At times there would not be even the five able-bodied men necessary to stand guard, so the weak and ill had to take their turns. They were suffering from boils, swellings, burning fevers and, always, the flux. Day and night the sound of pitiful groaning could be heard, with none to bring help to the ill. Master Hunt lay at death's door the whole month. Often three and four would die in one night. The living scarcely had strength to bury the dead.

The death of Bartholomew Gosnold on August 22 brought universal grief, for he had been one of the first to urge the colonization plan. Since he was a member of the Council, he was honored by a military funeral. All the ordnance in the fort was fired, and many volleys of small shot as well. President Wingfield read the service and declared that Gosnold's death had deprived the colony of its best hope of success and good fortune.

Cape Merchant Thomas Studley died on August 28, but by this time the storehouse was empty. The cooler weather of September brought help, but by now more than half the colonists were dead.

Neither President Wingfield nor George Kendall became ill, because they avoided any contact with the sick. Also, many suspected they were strengthened by their hidden supplies of food. They were using every opportunity to stir up dissension, and the situation finally became so acute that Kendall was removed from the Council and confined to the hold of the pinnace. Wingfield was held to be equally guilty, but because of his noble relatives, the colonists feared to do more than remove him from the presidency. John Ratcliffe was elected president. But at a later trial Wingfield confessed that he had secretly removed the oil and vinegar from the storehouse and buried it, along with two gallons each of sack and brandy, and he was then also deposed from the Council. At Master Hunt's request, the sack was set aside to be used for Holy Communion.

Captain Smith, meanwhile, had recovered sufficiently from his illness to be able to make short trading trips in the shallop up and down the river. Surprisingly, the Indians now seemed willing to let the colonists have small supplies of grain and venison. Also, there appeared in the river a great flock of water fowl, and they were able to bag some. For the moment there was food.

Returning from one of these trips, Smith learned that one of the laborers, to save himself from execution, had confessed that Wingfield and Kendall were plotting to take the pinnace and escape to England. This was more than could be borne. Kendall was convicted of treason and shot. It was decided that Wingfield was to be returned to England as soon as possible.

Such was the condition of the colony on the first of December. The bad element raised the complaint that no commands of the Company had been carried out, so Ratcliffe called a meeting of the Council to discuss the situation.

The meeting had been in progress for over an hour and Smith had taken no part in the discussion. Suddenly his heavy voice broke the momentary stillness. " 'Tis true, gentlemen, we have seemingly accomplished little in the last six months, but we are making no headway by sitting here talking all this afternoon. Unless we can settle the matter out of hand, I'd liefer be cleaving fuel."

A spectator would not have considered it a very attractive scene. The men were dressed in similar fashion, wearing coarse frieze doublets, leathern hose, Irish stockings and Monmouth caps. They were seated on wooden benches around a rough pine table. Against the portion of the wall behind each man was a musket.

"Captain Smith is ever given to deeds rather than words!" This speaker's voice told instantly that he was a gentleman. Despite his coarse clothing, one could see at a glance that his hands had never been accustomed to more important work than swordplay. As the only representative of nobility in the colony, he was always shown a special respect by the others.

"I would there were more like Captain Smith in that respect, Master Percy," said the man at the head of the table. "We have been in this good land of Virginia now for six months, and what have we done save bury our dead? Captain Newport will return anon and we shall be obliged to send a report back to the Company. What will that report be? As president, I felt it to be my duty to call a meeting to see what was in the minds of the other members of the Council."

Again the heavy voice of Captain Smith broke the silence. "Master Ratcliffe hath been president for so short a time that none should blame him for the little accomplished. But since no one hath solved our difficulty, though for several hours we have discussed the matter, I will volunteer to lead a band on an exploring expedition up the river which our Indian neighbors call the Chickahominy. Sam Collier reports that Wowinchopunk told him the source of this river is so near the sea that in times of storm the river is very salt."

"I fear me Wowinchopunk knoweth not the meaning of the truth, God help his poor soul!" Though this speaker was dressed in the conventional black cassock and gown of the Established Church, there was a musket leaning against the wall behind him. Master Hunt was always ready to share the dangers of his comrades, but his talent lay in quieting disturbances rather than in stirring them up. He was not an appointed member of the Council, but every man in the colony was glad to have the clergyman attend the meetings and give his opinion with the others.

Ratcliffe again spoke. "Captain Smith's suggestion is very wise. We have explored the river the savages call the Powhatan after their king, but which we call the James after our king.

I am convinced it will not give us the much-desired passage to the South Sea. In view of these rumors, it would be well to explore the Chickahominy also. Captain Smith, when do you prefer to set out?"

"Captain Newport is already overdue and will doubtless be here soon. If we do not set out immediately, we shall have no news to send back to the Company. I am ready to start on the trip so soon as may be. There will be no lack of volunteers to accompany me, I warrant."

While the tone of the last two speakers had been scrupulously polite, it was evident to the other members of the Council there was no love lost between them. Of the original councilors, one had died during the previous summer, one had been proven guilty of treason and shot, one had been expelled from the Council, and the fourth, Captain Newport, had returned to England. The vacancies had been filled temporarily, until directions could be had from the Company. Smith and Ratcliffe were leaders of rival factions in the colony, but through the diplomacy of Master Hunt they were ostensibly at peace.

The difference between the two men could easily be seen. Captain Smith was not yet thirty, but he had the appearance of a hardened and experienced soldier. His face was striking. He wore a bushy beard and a heavy mustache pushed back on either side to show a full, determined mouth. His forehead also served to emphasize his strong will, but the eyes had a merry, almost boyish look. Yet those kind eyes could show anger, and when the bushy brows were drawn down over them, men forgot they had ever looked merry. Ratcliffe was also a brave, experienced soldier, but his face would not inspire confidence. His small, beady eyes, unable to bear a direct gaze, suggested those of a skulking animal.

When Smith mentioned volunteers for the trip, two members spoke at once, asking to be included. Ratcliffe nodded. "Captain Archer and Captain Powell are evidently in favor of your plan, Captain Smith. If it be the pleasure of the Council, you may choose your own party and leave as soon as possible."

The councilors adjourned and joined their comrades who were outside the building. Captain Ratcliffe left the room first and walked down the path with a man who had evidently been waiting for him.

Smith paused in the door and watched the two disappearing figures. He turned to his companion, Master Percy. "Our sometime president seems to feel the sting of his expulsion," he said dryly, "but Ratcliffe keeps him well informed."

"Poor Wingfield!" said Percy sadly. "This trip has been a sad disappointment to him. He expected that long ere this he would have his pockets lined with precious stones."

"Instead of reaping treasure, he has reaped naught save dishonor. Now he will have to face his noble relatives at home. Pity him an you will, George. But as for me——" Leaving his sentence unfinished, he strode off to one of the huts.

Master Percy remained standing in the doorway of the room in which the meeting had been held. It was a strange scene before him. As he gazed about he thought with wry humor of the family's seats at Petworth and Syon. He could see two sides of the stockade forming their fort. This stockade enclosed a little more than an acre of land. It was triangular in shape. The crude houses of the settlers were in lines parallel to the sides of the fort, but were separated from the stockade by a street thirty feet wide. In the middle of the open space were the church, the storehouse and the guardhouse. The meeting had been held in the latter building. As he stood quietly looking at the uncouth buildings, the sun sank behind him, shedding its crimson light over the river. To the right he could see the white sails of the pinnace, the little twenty-ton *Discovery*, the only link between these wanderers and England. This ship had already been involved in a serious tragedy in the colony. It now rode at anchor a few feet from shore. A little to one side could be seen a lone cypress tree, showing green against the river. Across Back Creek was the forest, the unending forest. When the colonists had landed, this forest had been gay with all the beauties of spring. Then the more mature trees had been in full leaf, but the oaks had just been unfolding tiny red leaves, and the pale-yellow blooms of the poplar and the white dogwood had been in their full glory. Now the oaks and poplars cast their bare arms in the December wind. It was all dull and dark save where a gigantic cedar or pine made a green spot on the horizon.

A dull, uninteresting home, was it not? But many of these men did not look upon it as home. Most were bold adventurers, glad of another land to explore. When they built the rude little huts and constructed chimneys of wattles daubed with clay, they looked upon them merely as temporary shelters from heat and cold and never thought to spend more than a short time in them. They expected to return to England in a year or two with their pockets lined with gold and jewels, possibly after having made themselves famous by discovering a passage to the South Sea or by learning what had become of the lost colony of Roanoke. To be sure, the Virginia Company wished to establish a permanent colony, but these dashing men of the "First Supply" were willing to let those who came later do the less spectacular work.

CHAPTER III

A Voyage to the South Sea

Before the evening meal was finished, news had spread that Captain Smith was to lead an exploring expedition up the Chickahominy. For the past month the weather had been rough and time had hung heavy on the hands of these active men. Now they welcomed any plan to break the monotony of their lives.

The day after the Council meeting was cold and stormy, but that did not hinder preparations for the contemplated trip. Samuel Collier was sent to Wowinchopunk, the werowance of the neighboring Indians, to procure two guides. This boy was the chosen messenger because in some inexplicable way he had picked up enough of the Indian tongue to make himself understood. He returned just before nightfall, bringing with him two Paspahegh lads, who agreed to guide the party to the source of the Chickahominy River for a dozen beads apiece. Before the colonists went to their rest that night, everything was in readiness for the trip.

The sun had not yet risen when the whole colony gathered on the shore to watch the boat push off. After each man had taken his seat, the colonists bared their heads while Master Hunt offered a prayer for the safety of the travelers. At a word from Captain Smith, the rowers lowered the oars and the boat shot clear of the bank and turned its head up the river. There was a farewell shout from those on shore, and an answer rang merrily from the boat. There was no joy in the voices of those on the land, for they did not have the pleasure of anticipating the trip,

26

and the absence of these comrades would be keenly felt. Besides the two Indians and Captain Smith, the party was made up of Captains Archer and Powell, the two members of the Council who had so readily volunteered for service; Ensign John Waller and Master Jehu Robinson, two of Smith's warmest friends and partisans; Thomas Emery, John Laydon and George and William Cassen, four laborers; and Samuel Collier, Captain Smith's "boy."

Despite the cold wind and threatening clouds, the boat made good headway, and it was not long before they turned their little craft into the mouth of the Chickahominy. The channel of this river was not very deep even at its mouth, and they soon began to experience difficulty in pushing the boat ahead. Several times the Indians had to cut away overhanging trees or projecting roots that impeded the progress of the boat. It became evident a little after noon that they could not go any farther. When they reached a sort of open bay, Smith ordered the rowers to stop. All silently looked upstream.

"Methinks this river does not give us the passage we desire," said Captain Powell. "Yon channel is so narrow a canoe could scarcely make headway."

At this moment Sam Collier, who had been whispering to one of the guides, spoke. "Nemattanow says there is a canoe hidden in the bushes a little upstream."

Captain Smith's quick eyes were still taking in every detail of the landscape, and his plan was formed before he spoke. "This boat can go no farther, so 'twere well to push on upstream in the canoe. Also, we have no meat, and 'tis necessary to procure some. I will take two men and the guides and see what we can obtain." There was a rustle in the boat as he looked from one member of the party to another, contemplating which two should go with him. "Robinson and Emery may come with me; the others are to stay in the boat."

The boat pulled to the bank and the five men stepped out. Smith motioned the others to proceed and went back to the boat. "Captain Archer, I leave you in charge of the party. I shall probably be gone till nightfall. In the meantime do you keep in the middle of the stream, and in no case is anyone to land. Remember, Wowinchopunk has already shown himself to be tricky, and we are in his territory."

When Smith joined his companions who had proceeded up the river, the Indians had already dragged the canoe out of its hiding place and each had taken his seat. The three white men stepped in and the canoe shot upstream.

It was long past noon now and a sharp wind was whistling down the river. The men remaining in the boat had been out since early morning and were thoroughly chilled. Archer suddenly spoke. " 'Tis not in reason to stay in the midst of this river, where the wind can strike us. Pull toward the shore, boys. Mayhap the bank can break it off."

Powell started to protest, but refrained, for Archer held to strict military discipline when he was in command. For several minutes the only sound was the wind whistling through the dry leaves and bare branches. "There is wood enow within ten feet of the bank to warm us all," said George Cassen.

"Plague on it!" exclaimed Ensign Waller. "Make a fire. My fingers have well nigh lost all feeling now."

Cassen made a move to step out of the boat, and when Archer did not object, Powell kept silent no longer. "I should like to call to your mind, Captain Archer, our orders were to remain in the middle of the stream and no one was to leave the boat."

"Were you left in command, Captain Martin?" asked Archer curtly. "Get out and make that fire, Cassen."

Within five minutes there was a bright little blaze on the bank. Waller, not being content with the warmth he received in the boat, jumped out also and commenced to pile sticks on the fire. Then Captain Archer, William Cassen and John Laydon folowed, leaving only Powell and Sam Collier in the boat. Captain Powell picked up the oars to row back to the middle of the stream, but was sharply ordered to let the boat remain where it was.

"See that hickory log yonder, Cassen?" said Archer, pointing to a stout chunk lying near a thick undergrowth of bushes. "Fetch it here and lay it on the fire. Once it is caught, we shall have no more trouble with our fire till they return with supper."

George Cassen started toward the log, and others busied themselves piling small sticks and pine brush on the fire. Powell from the boat followed Cassen with his eyes. Powell saw him lean over and brace himself to lift the heavy log to his shoulder. At that moment a feathered scalp and a long, brown arm appeared. Before Powell could cry out, and before Cassen was aware of his danger, the Indian had leaped squarely onto his back and thrust his face into the leaves so that he could make no sound.

When the four men around the fire turned, the forest seemed suddenly alive with Indians. Archer, Waller and Laydon jumped toward the boat, but William Cassen started toward the thicket to aid his stricken brother. Powell called to him that he was being shut off from the boat, so he turned and ran back. An arrow struck him on the shoulder, but his stout coat turned it. Another whistled by his head. He threw himself on the ground and partly rolled, partly crawled and partly slid the rest of the distance. Powell and Waller caught his arms as he came within reach and dragged him into the boat. By this time the savages were on the bank, but a full load from the pistols of Archer and Laydon repulsed them somewhat. The boat was now in the center of the stream, almost out of reach of the arrows, so the men were able to row faster.

The Indians continued to stand on the bank, yelling, until the boat was lost from sight by a curve. Then they ran back to where a crowd had gathered around the unfortunate George Cassen. They lifted him to his feet and he found that his hands had been tied behind his back with a tight thong. One Indian asked him in which direction Captain Smith had gone. When Cassen did not reply, the savage grasped his scalp lock and, shaking his knife threateningly, repeated the question. Cassen silently pointed upstream. Instantly most of the Indians disappeared in that direction.

In the meantime Captain Smith, with his two comrades and the two guides, had rowed several miles upstream. All the while the river channel was becoming perceptibly smaller. Smith and Robinson discussed the situation while Emery and the Indians paddled the canoe. "Methinks 'tis useless to explore this channel farther. We had best stop and see what game we can kill, and return to the rest of the party. After a few days' hunting we can return to Jamestown. Mayhap we can find some Indians who will sell us corn. The supply is scarce."

A few minutes later the five men were on the bank. The Indians drew the canoe up on the land. Smith left Robinson and Emery to guard it, and took the two Indians into the forest. The Englishmen lay down on the ground so that the canoe would shelter them from the full force of the wind, and soon were asleep.

They were lying thus when a small party of Indians, some of those who had attacked the boat, crept stealthily forward. Robinson raised his head in time to see a knife plunged into Emery's back. Before he could reach for his gun, another Indian struck him on the head with a tomahawk. The Indians stopped only long enough to seize the pistols and muskets belonging to the dead men and then glided off in the direction Smith and the two guides had taken.

One of the guides had gone entirely out of sight, but Smith had kept with him the one Sam Collier had called Nemattanow. A suspicious rustling of the leaves caused Smith to turn. He was just in time to see an Indian skulking from one tree to another. Suspecting treachery, he seized Nemattanow, and jerking off his garter, he passed it around the Indian's body and arms and fastened it to a buckle on his coat of mail.

The savages were now upon him and he commenced to fire at them over Nemattanow's shoulder, at the same time moving backward. Every moment the savages increased in number, but they stood too much in awe of his gun to approach too near. Several arrows were shot, but he was so completely shielded by his captured guide that only one of them wounded him slightly.

All the while he was moving backward, hoping to reach the boat and firing as rapidly as he could. The Indians were dancing and yelling, but they were still afraid to come near him. Smith was beginning to hope he could make his escape, when suddenly he backed into a piece of muddy ground and sank several inches. He jumped to one side, but only sank deeper. He continued to flounder backwards a few more steps, sinking all the while. He cast a hasty glance over his shoulder and saw he was between a deep swamp and a hundred yelling savages. The mud was now over his knees and he could feel it still giving away. His struggles only caused him to sink deeper. He saw that it would mean death if he did not surrender, so he threw away his musket and motioned his captives to come and get him. With a final triumphant yell, they rushed for him and, after some difficulty, managed to pull Smith and Nemattanow out of the mud. They formed a circle around him and made a triumphal march to where Opechancanough, their chief, had set up a temporary court in the woods.

CHAPTER IV

Enter the Princess

Smith realized that only his wits could save him now. Hope of immediate escape was abandoned as soon as he saw his old enemy Wowinchopunk standing behind Opechancanough. Wowinchopunk and his warriors were striped with black paint. He had set out to capture Smith and by an evil chance had fallen in with the band of the powerful Opechancanough. Smith's approach was greeted by a fresh outburst of yells. He put his hand in his doublet and drew out a small ivory compass. With a profound bow, he presented it to Opechancanough. The savages seemed instantly to forget their anger, and all crowded around their chief. One by one they tried to touch the vibrating needle and gave a grunt of surprise when they encountered the glass. Finally Opechancanough looked to Smith for information.

He had been waiting for this and now stepped eagerly forward. Partly by gestures and partly by a mixture of English and the Indian language he explained to them that the earth was round. He told them that it revolved around the sun. His audience listened breathlessly. He told them of the powerful people living across the water and of the other nations inhabiting the earth. Not an Indian moved a muscle. He next told them of the powerful God the white men worshipped; that He loved his servants and was not like the terrible Okee, who sucked the children's blood. Smith did not stop till the warriors had ceased to finger their knives and tomahawks and were gazing at him with only interest in their faces.

When Smith's voice was finally silent, Opechancanough spoke to some of the young men, who bounded away to prepare supper. They returned with fish and maize cakes. The meal was eaten in silence. At its close Smith was led away to a place where brush had been piled up to break the wind, and with an Indian on each side of him, he lay down to sleep. He could see Opechancanough with his braves around him, and he knew they were discussing him, but for the night he felt safe. He thought of his companions—those in the boat, who were doubtless hurrying back to Jamestown; and the other two, whose dead bodies he had seen on the river bank. Then, commending his soul to God's care, he fell asleep.

At daybreak the warriors awoke. Some of the younger ones prepared breakfast, and soon they were ready to start out. No one spoke to Smith, so he disdained to ask questions. He saw that there were no preparations for his immediate death, but that they were preparing to take him on a journey. The sun was just tinting the clouds with a rosy light when the line of march was formed. Smith was carefully guarded. Three men held him fast by each arm, and on either side were six men in single file. It would have been useless to try to escape, so he did not make an attempt to do so. He devoted himself to learning what he could about his savage captors and the country.

A little before noon they approached a village and a large crowd came out to meet them. When the newcomers caught sight of Smith, the yells were deafening. Women and children crowded round him, for many had never seen one of the wonderful pale-faced strangers. The medicine men, rattling dried snake skins filled with copper, also came out.

There was a huge fire in the center of the village. The women spread mats around it and the men took their seats, with Smith in their midst. The women brought to them platters of boiled hominy, venison and cakes of chinquapin meal. A full supply was given Smith. After they had eaten, each of the warriors pulled out his pipe and filled it, first throwing a pinch of tobacco as an offering to Okee, or the One Alone, called Kiwassa.

The silent march was resumed. Toward night there could be seen in the distance the circle of mulberry trees that was an indication of a village. That night Smith slept for the first time in a wigwam. This was a shelter, oval in shape, made by planting saplings in the desired position and then bending their tops over and tying them together. It was covered with bark and grass. There was a hole at the top to allow smoke to escape. Across the door-opening was a mat. Smith was tied to a log and left alone. For a while he worked at his bonds, but soon discovered that when an Indian tied a knot, it stayed tied. During the night he heard the wind howling through the trees and in the morning there was a thin skim of snow on the ground. As soon as the morning meal was eaten, the march was resumed. All this day and the next it was continued. They passed through numerous villages, in which Smith was the center of attention.

On the evening of the third day they came to a large river. The Indians living on the bank provided canoes and the whole party was soon rowing upstream. Suddenly the rowers began to strike the water so softly as scarcely to cause a ripple. The Indians sat with bowed heads, some chanting a kind of wild song under their breath. Presently, one by one, they dropped different things in the river—tobacco, beads or arrows. Smith looked on in wonder. Presently he saw before them a group of low red hills, and on the highest of these were situated three long houses. Then he knew that they were approaching Uttamussac and the temples, where were kept the great image of Okee and the mummies of the dead kings.

A crowd greeted them on the bank. The population of the village was almost doubled by the number of visitors who had come to view the celebration of the capture of the white captain. Smith was led to a large wigwam. Two Indian girls appeared with his supper, venison and maize cakes. The quantity would have been sufficient for a dozen men. He remained alone, but all the while he could hear yelling outside and could see the light of a tremendous fire. Toward midnight two young men entered with more venison and maize cakes and a gourd of pohickory.

He ate a small portion and, after the young men left, fell asleep immediately. After day broke, another large supply of food was brought to him. By this time he had decided that he had been brought to this sacred spot to be the chief dish of a cannibal feast, and that they were trying to fatten him for the occasion. He resolved to lessen the amount he was eating, so he sent his breakfast away untouched.

Boys entered carrying wood and built a fire in the center of the hut. Suddenly a gigantic man came skipping in. His body had been oiled and bright-colored feathers were plastered all over him. His eyes were painted black. Around his neck and on his arms were skins of snakes and weasels. He was followed by six others, similarly decorated, three with their eyes painted red and three painted white. These were the priests of the great temple of Okee. Each man held a gourd filled with stones. Rattling these and chanting a dismal tune, they marched around Smith, trailing a circle of meal. Then they marched around him again and put down at intervals little heaps of corn. Next they took sticks and laid these between the corn. During the marching the rattling of the gourds and the chanting, which was punctuated with grunts and gesticulations, never ceased. This strange rite was repeated every three or four hours for three days.

On the morning of the fourth day the village woke early. Smith thought his last hour had come. Much to his surprise, the line of march was again formed, and they set out in a north-easterly direction. One of the guards told Smith they were on their way to Weromocomoco, the residence of Powhatan. Smith had already met this powerful Indian and knew that this visit to him would prove disastrous. In three more days they approached the Chief Place of Council.

Smith was put in a wigwam with a guard, with the usual fire and noise outside. He knew that his fate was being discussed and decided upon.

In the morning he was brought before Powhatan.

The savage court was truly an impressive spectacle. The chief was a tall, gaunt man with a sullen, sour look. He was seated in front of a fire, wrapped in a robe of raccoon skins. On each side of him was a young girl and behind him were several more. All had their cheeks and shoulders dashed with puccoon and wore necklaces and bracelets of shells. The men were grouped behind the girls.

Powhatan rose and stretched out his long, powerful arm. "Captain Smith," he said, "the red men and the white men cannot dwell together. Why do you come and seek to take our land from us? Were not your own hunting grounds large enough? We wish for ourselves our maize fields and our fish weirs. We have no boats to take us away, so the white man must leave. Three suns from now the red men will go against Jamestown. If Captain Smith joins himself to the red men, he will be set free and Powhatan will give him the country of the Capahowsick to rule forever."

Smith decided to make a show of bravery. "Go!" he shouted. "Let the red men go against Jamestown! The great guns the English brought in their ships will belch out fire and there will not be an Indian left. Send a paper from me to Jamestown and you will see for yourselves."

Powhatan consented to do this. Smith wrote a letter to Percy, telling him where he was and what had befallen him. He told him to show the guns to the two Indians and to load one of the cannon with a projectile and fire it into the trees. Two guides set out at once with this note and a small basket of corn. Smith was led back to his hut and remained there till the messengers could return.

The sun was setting on the second day when the two Indians rushed back to the town. They told Powhatan either Smith was a prophet or the paper could speak. Everything had happened as he had said. They had seen the big guns and one of them had thrown fire into a tree and had torn the branches off one side. When that had happened, they had run away.

Smith again was brought before Powhatan. One of Powhatan's wives brought him water in a wooden bowl and another gave him a bunch of feathers on which to wipe his hands. Then some young girls brought him food. All the while he was eating, the Indians were silent. When he had finished Powhatan rose.

"Powhatan has said the white men must leave. What he says, he will do. If Captain Smith will help him drive out the white men, he can live, but since he refuses, he must die." He made a gesture of command to two men, who dragged forward two large stones and placed them in front of Powhatan. Two Indians seized Smith and forced him down on the stones. Two others raised clubs. He closed his eyes and gave himself up for dead, when he heard a shriek and felt arms thrown around his head. He opened his eyes and saw above him an Indian girl. She was dressed in a robe of doeskin lined with down from the breasts of pigeons and had strings of coral on her arms and neck. In her hair was a heron's plume, the badge of royalty. She was kneeling by Smith with her arms about his head, but her face was turned toward Powhatan. The old chief looked sternly toward the girl, and when she returned his direct gaze, his face gradually relaxed into a smile. One of the men tried to push her out of the way, but with another cry, she seized Smith convulsively and laid her head down upon his head.

The men with the clubs did not make another attempt to move the girl, and she did not release her hold on Smith. Again she looked toward Powhatan. When she saw his face, she gave him a quick, bright answering smile and slowly rose to her feet but kept her station near Smith.

Powhatan motioned Smith to rise, and he did so. He took his stand near the little maid to whom he owed his life. Powhatan made a lengthy speech, most of which Smith did not understand. But he managed to gather that his life was to be spared because Pocahontas, Powhatan's dearest daughter, desired it. Powhatan was ready to adopt him into his family as one of his sons. He wished to swear eternal friendship with Smith and still was ready to give his son the country of Capahowsick.

Smith thanked him enthusiastically but said he must first go back to Jamestown. Powhatan seemed loath to let him go, but finally said, "Stay and feast for ten suns and make bells and beads for Pocahontas, and then Powhatan will send you back to Jamestown."

Smith's first Christmas in Virginia was a strange one. The Indian village was gay. The days were a long succession of feasting and dancing. As Smith was enjoying the abundance the Indians provided, he thought of his companions at Jamestown and wondered if they were feasting also. He longed to go back, but knew it would not be possible till the time Powhatan had set.

Pocahontas was Smith's constant companion. He was glad to have her near him, for he felt safer when she was there. She was a slender little maid, fond of decking herself with all sorts of finery. According to his instructions, Smith spent his time making toys and ornaments for her. She showed an eager desire to learn English, and when Smith left, she was able to speak English more fluently than he could use the Indian language.

At last the time came for his departure. Powhatan made a long speech of farewell. Smith, seeing a reply was expected, recited one of Cicero's orations, which impressed his hearers greatly. During the celebration Pocahontas slipped away, and though Smith asked for her, he did not see her again.

It was the first week in January when the little party left Weromocomoco, and two days later it came in sight of the peninsula and the little palisaded fort.

CHAPTER V

The Princess to the Rescue

As Smith, accompanied by his guides, came in sight of the little town, his heart gave a glad leap. For three weeks he had seen no other human beings but Indians. Now, as he once more approached his comrades, he rejoiced. It was Sunday morning and the little party was walking rapidly, for Smith wished to take his Indian friends to the morning service. As they crossed the narrow isthmus, his ears strained to hear the bell. The remaining quarter of a mile was soon covered. As they drew near the palisade, his look became worried. He could see no sign of life in the fort. He glanced hastily in the direction of the river and stopped short in astonishment. The pinnace was not in its accustomed position, and even as Smith looked, he could see it changing position. At the same time the sound of excited voices was heard.

The stockade gate on the side toward the isthmus was open and unguarded. Smith ran through it and hastened across the triangular space. He jumped upon a platform on which was mounted a large falcon and from which he now had a clear view of the river. On the beach were gathered some twenty-odd men, all running up and down, shouting in the greatest excitement. They were turned toward the river, pointing at the pinnace. The anchor of the little vessel was raised and it was slowly shifting about so as to drop downstream. In a moment Smith loaded the falcon, seized the linstock and aimed toward the vessel. "A murrain take you!" he shouted at the top of his powerful voice. "Rascals, poltroons, stay or sink!" There was a puff of smoke and a ball struck the water not ten feet from the vessel.

"O Lord! a deliverer at last!" exclaimed Master Hunt.

The voices of the others were drowned in the general confusion.

"Drop the anchor!" commanded Smith. "Stay or sink! Stay or sink!" Another ball passed through the rigging. The anchor fell. "Lower the boat and come ashore—else, in God's name, I'll blow the ship to pieces!"

The boat was slowly lowered and a dozen men got into it. Smith kept his station at the falcon. "Captain Powell, arrest the ringleaders and put them in irons. I'll shoot again, an there's any resistance!" he called toward the boat. "What does this mean, George?" he demanded of Master Percy, who had run toward him.

"We're starving, Jack, starving!" said Percy in a low, tense voice. For three days now we have had naught but barley water. Wingfield stole what little we had left, and had all but escaped. We were left without any victual at all. Even good Master Hunt—look at him—he would not have lived a se'ennight."

The boat was now emptied and Smith and Percy joined the crowd on the beach. Wingfield and Ratcliffe, in irons, were the center of attention. Smith looked at them sternly. "Captain Powell, place the prisoners in the hold. Detail men to guard them. As for the rest of you"—turning toward the other men who had been in the boat—"I do not order you to be ironed, as we have need of your services. But hark ye—one man has been shot for this same crime, and you will be watched."

The crowd slowly broke into excited groups. Two of the men who had landed drew off a little distance from the others. One was Captain Archer. "Who put Smith in command?" he snarled to his companion. "Come with me, Martin, and I will show you who is master in this town."

Smith, Percy and Master Hunt walked back into the palisade and entered Hunt's dwelling, where there was a blazing fire.

"Here's a coil to get ourselves into on a Sabbath morning," said Smith.

"Thank the Lord you came in time, Captain Smith. We had been dead men in a week an they had escaped."

"Either Wingfield or I leave the colony at the first opportunity," answered Smith. "Our honored president is also in trouble, and who is to take command in his stead?"

"There is but one man who is strong enough to preserve us," said Percy with a feeble smile, "and methinks he has put himself in charge already. Now that you are with us again, they can be held under. Wingfield openly rejoiced when your letter to me came, and I have been fearful ever since."

"What victuals are on hand?" asked Smith abruptly.

"Practically none," Percy answered. "Newport is long overdue, and 'twill be six months ere we can grow food for ourselves. We shall have to depend on our Indian neighbors, and I fear me we shall get a scarce supply."

"No persuasion will induce me to starve. Don't lose heart, George," said Smith cheerfully. "With God's help we'll weather the gale. Ha! Captain Martin, what's toward now?"

"I am instructed by Captain Archer, who is Acting President of the Council till Captain Ratcliffe be released, to notify you that under the Levitical law you are guilty of the death of Master Robinson and Emery, since 'twas by your fault they were led to their sad end. You are to report to him for trial on the morrow."

Masters Hunt and Percy gasped in astonishment. Smith gazed at the newcomer in silence and then stepped toward him threateningly. His brows were closely drawn. His whole attitude indicated anger at white heat, but he spoke quietly and in a low voice. "John Martin, when will you cease to be a cat's-paw? Dost think to daunten me with an idle threat? Did I believe you capable of originating that scheme, inside of half an hour you would be in the hold of the pinnace. Our learned lawyer cooked it up. I ignore your insolent message, but as you value your life,

I warn you to be more careful how you perform errands for men who dare not risk their own skins. Master Percy, do you detain Captain Martin for a while. Captain Archer's message is of too great importance to brook delay, so I'll e'en report to him now." As he went out of the door, he met Captain Powell. "Ah, Nat, what have you done with those two rascals?"

"I have them safe in the hold of the pinnace. They are in irons and Ensign Waller is guarding them. Sam Collier is on shore guarding the boat and has orders to allow none to use it without permission."

"Come with me, Nat, and I'll deliver another charge to your keeping. Hello, John Laydon! We need your help."

In a few moments Archer was conducted on board the pinnace and placed under the same guard as the other two schemers. Smith strode back to Master Hunt's house. "You may go, Martin," he said. "Mayhap you will keep out of mischief now that your three tempters are out of the way." As Martin sullenly left the room, Smith dropped wearily into a seat. "A poor substitute for Sabbath bells," he said quietly.

There was a sudden commotion on the outside and Smith jumped to his feet as a boy burst into the room. "The guard at the west gate says Indians are coming over the neck of land."

"Call the men to arms!" Smith shouted as he ran. The fear was upon him that Powhatan's friendship was a mask, and the Indians were attacking the town. He jumped upon a platform on which a falcon was mounted, and looked eagerly toward the mainland. A crowd of ten or more Indians could be seen advancing slowly through the woods. They were bending under heavy burdens. As they came into an open space, Smith saw, to his astonishment, that a girl was in command of the party. The next moment he sprang down from the platform and ran out of the gate.

As he appeared, the Indians stopped hesitatingly, and then the girl broke into a run. "Captain! Captain!" she called, holding out her hands.

"Child, what's amiss now?" he asked as he advanced toward her.

She pointed to the ten Indian boys behind her. "Venison and maize," she said slowly, beckoning the boys to come forward. Each boy carried a large basket filled, as the girl had said, with venison and corn.

"The Lord provides for His own!" exclaimed Master Hunt fervently. "Captain Smith, who is the little brown angel who succors us in our dire extremity?"

Smith took the child's hand in his own and faced the crowd that had gathered. "Comrades," he said a little huskily, "this is Pocahontas, the daughter of the mighty chief Powhatan. Two weeks ago, at Weromocomoco, she saved my life when my brains were all but dashed to pieces. Again, by furnishing food at this time, she saves the lives of all."

The girl's quick eyes had been taking in every detail of the palisaded fort, the vessel and the men before her. As Smith ceased speaking, she gave him a bright smile, and then an expression of gravity settled on her face. The Indian boys had carried their baskets into the palisade. Smith, detecting the look of curiosity on their faces, showed them about. Pocahontas kept close to him all the while. She was interested in everything, but only occasionally did she ask a question. Her manner was self-possessed, but when any other than Smith spoke to her, she seemed shy. She was delighted with the trinkets the men gave her. The sun was setting when the savage visitors departed. Smith tried to persuade them to remain till the evening service, but at the sound of the bell they fled into the forest.

It was with thankful hearts that the men gathered in their rude little church. In the opening prayer, when Master Hunt asked for special blessing to descend upon Pocahontas, every heart echoed, "Amen."

A general meeting of the colony was held the following day and by popular vote Smith was asked to take command. No immediate move was to be made to punish the three traitors, for they were out of harm's way for the time being, and the arrival of Newport was daily hoped for. Nor had the colonists long to wait. Within a week the welcome cry of "A sail!" was heard and the whole colony hastily gathered on the beach. It was Captain Newport. He had on board some sixty settlers who had come to share the fortunes of the pioneers.

Newport gazed with dismay at the thirty-eight gaunt, emaciated men drawn up to receive him.

"Thank God, you have come in time!" said Master Percy. "The succor you are bearing is sorely needed."

" 'Tis little succor I bring," replied Newport. "Yellow fever broke out among us while we were at the Canaries, and a score of the colonists died. The inhabitants refused to let us land to replenish our supply of food and sweet water. My supply is sadly low."

"But did you not bring other comforts and necessities?" asked Percy anxiously.

Newport bowed respectfully to him. "Your noble brother, my Lord of Northumberland, had his agent deliver to our care the thirty muskets you directed me to bring, as well as a supply of new apparel. They are on the pinnace." He looked anxiously toward the river. "Has not the *Phoenix* yet arrived?"

"We have seen no vessel save yours," said Smith. "Did another sail with you?"

"The pinnace *Phoenix*, commanded by Captain Nelson, crossed with us, but just outside the capes there was a heavy fog and a mighty wind and I have seen no more of her."

Newport's eyes continued to search the crowd anxiously. "I have dispatches from the London Company for the Council. Has Master Wingfield——"

"Master Wingfield is in good health," interrupted Smith dryly, "but he is no longer president. In truth, he is now in the hold of the *Discovery*, charged with mutiny."

Captain Martin pushed his way to Newport's side. "All is in combustion here," he whispered. "Captain Smith claims that Master Wingfield must needs be executed for his crime, and

Master Wingfield and Captain Archer insist that Captain Smith should be executed for murder." Then his hunger for news caused him to forget his present troubles. "What word do you bring from my father?"

"Have done with talk of executions!" boomed Newport. "I, too, am a member of the Council and I bring with me a new member, Master Matthew Scrivener, appointed by the king to a seat on the Council. We will have a meeting on the morrow." Then he lowered his voice. "Your honored father, Sir Richard, continues as Master of the Royal Mint. He is so desirous we should find gold, he has sent over two goldsmiths and two refiners to aid in our search. But tell me, what's amiss with Master Hunt? Had it not been for his vestments, I had scarcely known him. You, too, look puny."

"In truth, I have been ailing since last summer. We had a plague of flux and fever. Many died. Master Hunt has not recovered his strength. Another illness would do for him, and we can ill spare him."

CHAPTER VI

A Trading Expedition and Its Results

With the arrival of Newport and his settlers, Jamestown took on new life. After nine months of loneliness the colonists were eager for news from home. Much to Smith's disgust, Newport insisted on releasing the three culprits after he heard their defense that during Smith's absence a Council meeting had been held and it had been decided to send the *Discovery* back to England for supplies.

Ratcliffe claimed his place as president and, after some disturbance, was allowed to keep it. Smith, Newport and Martin still held their places. Powell and Archer were elected to the places made vacant by Wingfield's expulsion and Kendall's execution.

There was a varied assortment among the company Newport brought. Over half the number were gentlemen, and following in their wake were a number of tailors, a jeweler and a perfumer. There were also a large number of laborers. Two of the gentlemen were Masters Nathaniel Causy and Jeffrey Abbott, old comrades of Smith. Another was Michael Sicklemore, an acquaintance of Captain Ratcliffe.

Two days later the cry "Indians!" was raised and Pocahontas again appeared. Newport seized upon this opportunity to send some presents he had brought for Powhatan—a red coat, a white dog and a fancy hat. A few days later more Indians appeared, bringing a magnificent pair of antlers for Newport, "the Great White Father"—words Smith had used in telling Powhatan about

46

Newport. Powhatan sent an invitation for Newport to visit him. Newport received the message with great consternation. "Dost think I would trust myself in the power of that wily savage?" he demanded half angrily.

"Pooh, pooh, man!" returned Smith. "There's naught to fear. 'Tis a friendly message."

"I have heard enough of his friendliness and I value my life too highly to put it in his power."

" 'Twould fare badly with us were we to offend Powhatan now. Had it not been for the little maid, I doubt you would have found us alive when you arrived. There's no danger so you go in a boat and take armed men."

"Since there's naught to fear, suppose you accompany me," sneered Newport. "No doubt your last visit with Powhatan was so pleasant you are eager to repeat it."

Smith only laughed, and two days later they set out with twenty armed men and trinkets that would please the savages. A band of Indians came out to meet them. Newport was dismayed by the bridges over the creeks. They were made of a few poles tied together by the bark of trees, and he suspected they were traps. He insisted that some of the Indians cross over first, and he held back the chief ones as hostages. Then half the soldiers crossed and formed a guard to protect the remainder of the party.

They found Powhatan sitting in state, surrounded by his wives and warriors. Pocahontas was present and greeted her old friend with a bright, winning smile. Powhatan rose to make the customary speech of welcome. "Powhatan is glad to see the Great Father. When the Great Father left at the end of the moon of blossoms, the red men thought he would come no more. Since my son"—pointing to Smith—"found favor with Pocahontas, the red men and the white men are at peace, and the red men will sell corn."

After this there was a feast, and at its close the peace pipe was brought out. An old man filled it with tobacco, lit it and bore it to the chief. The colonists were already familiar with Indian tobacco. Roanoke colonists had brought some back to Sir Walter

Raleigh, saying that the Indians had said that it would cure
men of being tired. Queen Elizabeth had been induced to try it,
and had said chokingly that it was a vegetable of singular strength
and power. George Percy, as a boy, had seen his noble brother
and Sir Walter smoking it, so he had obtained some from the
Indians and had introduced it to the other colonists. They had
noticed that the earthen pipes used by the Indians were much
larger than the ones Englishmen used, and that the bowls were
fastened together with copper. Because of these large bowls, the
colonists had reported that the Indians "dranck" their tobacco.
Powhatan smoked in silence, then passed the pipe to Newport,
who, in turn, passed it to Smith. After one or two puffs Smith
rose. "May the smoke of the calumet ever float above the red
men and the white men." A grunt of assent passed round the
circle.

After this ceremony Powhatan seemed eager to commence
the trade. Newport opened the box. He held up a gay red
blanket. "How much corn?" he asked.

"Captain Newport," said Powhatan, " 'tis not agreeable with
my greatness to trade in a peddling manner. Place before me
what you have to sell, and I will pay you its worth. You also
are a great chief, and it is not well for us to act like children."

"Whist, man!" muttered Smith, "do no such thing! The ras-
cal but wishes to cheat you."

"I can manage this business, friend," replied Newport curtly.
He threw the contents of the box on the ground.

Powhatan surveyed the pile carelessly and indicated the arti-
cles he wished to keep. He spoke to the young men and they
brought a four-bushel basket of corn. Newport flew into a
rage. At first Powhatan seemed surprised, but when he finally
understood Newport's words, a dangerous light came in his eyes.
Smith thought it time to interfere, so he drew out of his doublet
a long string of blue beads.

Powhatan's attention was at once attracted. He held out his
hand for the beads, but Smith shook his head. Powhatan had
another large basket of corn brought in, but Smith made a move

to put the beads back in his doublet. A larger basket of corn was placed before Smith, which he pretended not to see. Suddenly he stretched the string to its full length. "The beads are made of something wonderful, the color of the sky. None save the greatest kings on earth can wear them." Then he thrust them out of sight.

"What does my son wish?" demanded Powhatan eagerly.

"Corn," replied Smith. "Corn to last the white men till the corn-gathering season shall come and they will have enough for themselves."

Without hesitation Powhatan ordered the young men to put corn on the little vessel. Basket after basket was emptied, till fully three hundred bushels were on board.

Powhatan made a long speech of farewell, and the Indians looked to Smith for a reply. He had learned that they appreciated a long string of words even if they did not understand what was being said. So he told them of his early adventures. He was once among a shipload of Roman Catholics when a mighty storm arose. He was thrown overboard because they thought he was the cause of the storm. But God took care of him and saved his life. Next he told of his fight with three Turks, when he cut off their heads, one after another. Finally he told how he was wounded in battle and left on the field to die. The enemy found him and sold him into slavery, but he beat out the brains of his cruel master and escaped to England.

The Indians listened carefully, occasionally giving grunts of surprise. Then the white men were escorted to their boat. Newport, as an evidence of the love he bore Powhatan, left with him a thirteen-year-old boy, Thomas Savage, who had just arrived. Powhatan, in return, gave Newport a young Indian, Namontack, recommending him as being of shrewd and subtle capacity. As they sailed down the York River, they could see Powhatan playing with the beads while the pile of things Newport had brought lay unheeded before him.

When they reached Jamestown, everyone was in a state of great excitement. One of the refiners insisted he had found a

rich deposit of gold. In two days quite an amount had been col-
lected. On account of the unusual supply of corn obtained from
the Indians, it was decided to indulge in a feast. After supper the
crowd divided into several groups. Smith, Percy, Scrivener,
Powell and several others retired to Master Hunt's cabin and
enjoyed their pipes in peace. In Ratcliffe's cabin there was a
different scene. Wingfield, Newport, Archer, Martin and others
were drinking and dicing. Ratcliffe had been moody ever since
Newport had arrived. The newcomer, Sicklemore, had been
spending much time in Ratcliffe's company despite the sour looks
and sarcastic thrusts he received. Since no one else in the colony
knew him, all were at a loss to explain the attitude of the two
toward each other. Ratcliffe had been drinking heavily and his
ugly nature was aroused. Sicklemore appealed to Martin to verify
a statement Ratcliffe had made.

"Dost doubt my word, fellow?" demanded Ratcliffe.

"Master Ratcliffe's past reputation for truth is too well proven
for me to doubt his word now," sneered Sicklemore.

"Villain, I'll make you eat those words!" roared Ratcliffe,
flinging himself toward Sicklemore. The other men parted hastily
so as to give the floor to the two adversaries. In their eagerness
to see the fight, none of those present noticed that a blazing pine
knot had fallen among some clothing. Suddenly a tongue of
flame leaped up the side of the hut and caught the thatched roof.
The men rushed outside, and their shouts brought the other
colonists into the triangle. It was impossible to fight the flames,
so the frightened colonists saved what they could. Master Hunt
suffered the most serious loss, for his whole library was burned.
He used his little strength helping others to save their blankets
and wearing apparel.

A dismal scene greeted the men when dawn came. All that
was left of the fort was a few charred logs of the palisade and
great piles of smoldering ashes. A Council meeting was held.
Smith wished to rebuild at once, but most of the others preferred
to dig for gold. Finally Smith gained permission to take with him
such men as were willing to forgo the digging and begin cutting

trees for the new palisade. Smith went where practically the whole colony was at work. Martin was superintending.

"Come on, boys," said Smith cheerily, "let's clear away the ruins."

"That can wait, Smith," replied Martin. " 'Tis best to get the metal out of the ground while Newport is here, so he can take it back."

"What will we do for shelter and protection?" urged Smith.

"We can sleep on the vessel," answered Martin. "You help us here, Smith, and then we'll lend a hand with the logs."

"No!" answered Smith angrily. "Here's one who is not enamored of your dirty skill to load a drunken ship with gilded mud."

Smith gathered together a few of the boys and, with Scrivener's help, commenced to cut logs for the palisade. The work of digging gold progressed rapidly, and two months later the ship was loaded and set sail. In addition to the dirt, Newport had on board twenty turkeys, his Indian boy Namontack and the disgraced Wingfield. Archer, whose doubtful skill at law had caused so much trouble, also decided to leave. In spite of the ruling of the London Company that no one was to send back from the plantation any word of discouragement, a letter from one of the new colonists slipped through, begging his relatives to send "old clothes, large or small, doublets, trousers, stockings, capes, or whatever may appear fit." He also asked for paper and ink, for "we need everything."

During these two months the little Indian princess frequently visited Jamestown. Smith was her warmest friend, but she soon won the love of all. Master Hunt took special interest in her, and told of the God the English worshiped. Her interest was so great that in public prayers he regularly mentioned the "dear and blessed **Pocahontas.**"

CHAPTER VII

The Heart of the Princess

Newport had no sooner left for England than Smith commenced to urge the rebuilding of the burned town. More than two months had gone by since the fire, and the men had suffered greatly. Indeed, some of the weaker ones had died of exposure. With the help of Scrivener and some sailors Smith had succeeded in building a new church and several houses. These were rude little structures with raftlike sides against which was packed a mixture of sedge and earth. The interiors were plastered with a coarse clay found on the island. As yet there had been no attempt to replace the palisade. It was also time to plant corn, so the colonists could not complain of lack of work.

Ten days later a sail was seen. The colonists seized their arms and gathered on the beach. They were in constant fear of an attack by the Spaniards, so fear as well as hope was aroused at the sight of a sail. The ship proved to be friendly. It was the *Phoenix,* which had become separated from Newport outside the Virginia capes. When Captain Nelson had seen how far off his course he had been blown, he had wisely turned back to the West Indies and spent the winter there. The new settlers he brought increased the population of Jamestown to more then one hundred men.

"More hungry mouths to feed," grumbled Captain Martin.

"Not so, my friend," replied the genial Nelson. "I kept my men at work and in good health while gathering foodstuffs on the islands. My hold is bulging with victuals, which I will impart freely to all."

"A happy change from Newport," said Percy to Smith. "What we obtained from Newport had to be paid for dearly. I knew not whether he was selling from his own store or from that meant for the colony. The bills of exchange on my brother that he took back the last time were large. But my noble brother does not grudge me necessities, or even luxuries."

"Such as the feather bed, bolster, blankets and tapestry covering Master Nelson brought?" inquired Smith mischievously.

Percy flushed uncomfortably. " 'Tis well he sent them, for all I had were burned. And I had used up my store of paper, ink, wax and soap. I could wish he had sent a few clothes, also."

"And where do you propose to store all these necessities?" Smith persisted.

"The ship's carpenter has contracted to build a house for me ere they leave. I am giving him a letter to my brother, so he knows he will be paid. What is wrong with that?" His tone was now resentful. Smith laughed indulgently and said no more.

There had been no trouble with the Indians since early winter. Wowinchopunk, the chief disturber up to this time, seemed to have gone away, and through Pocahontas, trouble with Powhatan was avoided. Then an event occurred that foreboded evil. Powhatan sent a number of turkeys to Jamestown, requesting that a sword for every turkey be sent to him.

Smith received the message, which he at once gave to Ratcliffe. "What does the savage mean?" he inquired.

"I thought Newport would cause trouble when he sent those swords to Powhatan," replied Ratcliffe.

"Sending swords to Powhatan?" gasped Smith. "What dost mean, man? Out with it!"

"Powhatan sent twenty turkeys to Newport and asked for swords. Newport was fearful of offending him, so sent the swords."

"An my opinion bear any weight, we shall not repeat that foolish act. The savages have means enow for harming us, without our supplying them with arms."

For a week no one thought of the occurrence. Master Hunt

was the first to foretell evil. "The little maid hath not been here for many days," he remarked one evening.

"Not since the day before we received the turkeys and refused to send the swords," answered Scrivener. "Can it be that Powhatan is forgetting the peace between the red men and the white men?"

Since he had been so long delayed, Captain Nelson wished to return to England as soon as possible, and the Council took up the discussion of the return cargo. Smith vigorously opposed any delay in the spring planting.

Percy disagreed with him. "Why worry about planting? 'Tis the duty of the London Company to provision us. They have directed us to spend our time sending back commodities to them. They must have a return for the money they have invested."

"And in the meanwhile we starve! Did Newport leave sufficient when he went back? Did he return in twenty weeks, as he promised? How much did he leave after this last voyage? Because Captain Nelson has supplied us for the moment, can we hope it will last us till another ship from England comes? We do well to provide for ourselves."

In the end Smith's advice was ignored. Martin, acting no doubt on the urging of his father, the Master of the Mint, urged them to search for another vein of ore. But Captain Nelson threw his weight in favor of a load of cedar logs. Smith found one thing to commend. "At least we are clearing ground that can later be planted, so we have not lost the season."

Wowinchopunk was again seen in the neighborhood and went back to his old habit of annoying any settlers he found working at a distance from the settlement. No active measures were taken till one day six men, including Smith, were attacked. That doughty soldier immediately called a force of men together. He scoured the woods around Jamestown and had several skirmishes with the Indians. He took several savages prisoner and carried them to Jamestown as hostages for the rest. The Indians made the next move. John Laydon and Sam Collier were working in the woods just across the neck of land, when they were suddenly attacked by a large force and taken prisoner. The Indians sent word to Jamestown that the men would be put to death if the captured Indians were not released at once. Smith was now fully aroused. The men were called to arms and proceeded across the isthmus into the woods. Within two hours the Indians were so thoroughly punished they begged for peace and restored the captives.

In the last skirmish Smith caught sight of Nemattanow, who will be remembered as one of the guides on the trip up the Chickahominy. He immediately seized the Indian and detained him when the others retreated. "What mean these onsets, Nemattanow?" he demanded.

The Indian sullenly shook his head and pretended not to understand. "Come, come," said Smith. "You take my meaning well enow. So you do not wish to be the eighth Indian in the gaol, you'll find your tongue. It ill fits the red men to break the peace after they have buried the hatchet. What's amiss with Powhatan and Wowinchopunk? Hold! Mayhap this will quicken your wits"—and he suddenly drew his sword and pricked the Indian on the arm.

Unlike most Indians, Nemattanow had shown he was both a bully and a coward. When he felt the touch of cold steel, he quickly moved out of the way and spoke. "Powhatan sent us to bring to him the sticks that speak."

Smith gazed at him so steadily that the fellow again showed signs of fear. "Go tell Powhatan that ere long he will have enow of the sticks that speak, so these onsets do not cease. The seven men at Jamestown will not be set free till Powhatan again shows himself to be friendly."

The party returned to Jamestown and reported that all seemed quiet. " 'Tis a pity these poor savages hear so much more of our muskets than they do of our prayers," said Master Hunt regretfully.

"Good Master Hunt forgets that our wily neighbors are none too good to feign to pray while they draw tomahawks from their belts," muttered Smith to Percy.

Now that the Indians were quiet, the work of loading the
Phoenix with logs progressed more rapidly. Smith and Scrivener,
especially, urged the work forward, for the crop had not yet been
planted nor the palisade rebuilt. After the supply of gold was
exhausted, most of the gallants refused to work. As half of the
colony was composed of gentlemen, there were many idle hands.
Ratcliffe, in particular, was a constant source of worry to Smith,
Scrivener and the few others who were eager to push forward
the necessary work. He was a bold soldier, but no persuasion
could induce him to take part in any necessary work. Indeed,
the time of one of the boys was pretty well taken up with waiting
on him.

Early one morning about a week after the last encounter
with the savages, Smith started out alone across the neck of land
leading to the mainland. The sun had just risen and the dew was
on the grass. He was walking rapidly, whistling softly to himself
as he drank in the delight of the early June morning. Suddenly
he stopped in surprise, for a few feet in front of him stood
Pocahontas. He had often noticed the gravity of her features,
but now he saw there was an unusual look of sadness in her
eyes. She did not run to meet him as she generally did, but stood
still, waiting for Smith to make the first advance. "Child!" he
exclaimed, holding out his hands in his usual greeting. "What
means this? Is aught amiss?"

She gave a glad little cry and ran toward him, her bright
smile breaking over her face. "Art angry with me, Captain?"
she asked timidly.

"Nay, nay, little maid. You have done naught to make me
angry," he said gently. "But who is this?" he asked as he noticed
an Indian boy leaning against the tree.

"My brother, Nantauquas," the girl replied, drawing the boy
forward. The lad was a slender fellow, a little taller than his
sister. He was a warrior in miniature. A big eagle feather was
stuck in his hair and a gaudy quiver hung over his shoulder. He
carried a bow and in his belt was a tomahawk. His body was
heavily oiled and the muscles on his arms and legs showed fine

physical development. He bore himself proudly, as if he were conscious of his position as a king's son. He greeted Smith shyly but with a touch of haughtiness in his manner.

"Why didst think I might be angry, child?" Smith asked Pocahontas.

"I bring no more maize now for many suns," she replied, "and my people, the red men, have forgotten, have done——" She stopped in confusion.

". . . have forgotten that the red men and the white men have buried the hatchet," Smith finished for her.

" 'Tis that I mean," she replied, nodding. "But," she went on eagerly, " 'tis not by Powhatan's orders. Powhatan has sent a message to Wowinchopunk to cease troubling his friends. He wishes you to know he still loves the white men, and he sent me to tell you. Dost believe me, Captain?"

"I believe we have found at least one heart of gold among the aborigines," replied Smith. Then, seeing the puzzled look on her face, he went on: "I believe *you*, my little maid, and pray God's blessing on the child who lives by the Golden Rule, though she may never have heard it."

"God," she repeated softly. "He is the one Master Hunt says the white men worship instead of our terrible Okee. Is it not so?"

"Yea, my child," he replied gently.

She stood silent, and when she lifted her eyes to Smith again, the sad look had returned to them. "Captain, dost mean to keep our men at Jamestown?" When Smith did not reply, she went on slowly, " 'Tis true they have done you harm, but I would not see them unhappy. So you'll turn them free, they'll trouble you no more. I—I love them, too, Captain."

Smith lifted her drooping head and saw that her eyes were full of tears. "Come with me, little one," he said softly, turning toward the town, "and you, too, Nantauquas."

The town was awake when Smith and his two charges entered it. The boy cooks had breakfast ready and the little prince and princess graciously accepted an invitation to eat with the colonists. Pocahontas was now on friendly terms with Powell and

Master Hunt, but she had little to say to any of the others. Nantauquas did not speak, but his bright eyes took in every detail of the white man's home. After the meal was over, Smith had the keeper of the gaol release the seven prisoners.

"And prithee, Captain Smith, by what authority do you give such an order?" demanded Ratcliffe.

"Who took them captive, sirrah, and placed them in the gaol?" Smith retorted.

"When you placed them in the gaol, they passed from your keeping into that of the Council," sneered Ratcliffe.

"Dost wish to call a meeting of the Council to decide the question? 'Twill be but an easy matter. Ho, Scrivener!"

"Nay, nay, my good friend," replied Ratcliffe condescendingly, "your willingness to consult your fellow councilors removes my scruples."

Smith strode off without replying. He went across the neck of land with his two visitors and the captives. "Child," he said to Pocahontas, "tell Powhatan 'tis for your sake only these men go free. Good-by, little maid; good-by, Nantauquas." The boy solemnly returned the salute.

Ratcliffe watched Smith and the Indians out of sight, his small eyes glittering with hatred. He then turned to one of his constant companions. "An that poltroon does not kill himself on this new voyage he is planning, we shall have to find some surer means to get him out of the way."

CHAPTER VIII

Enter the Ladies

The cargo of cedar logs was now ready, so the *Phoenix* made preparations to return to England. Master Martin, who had never fully recovered from his severe illness of the previous summer, sailed on her. For the same reason, many tried to persuade Master Hunt to leave also. He gently refused to go. "My heart is in Virginia. An my body fails, let it lie here also."

It had been decided that another voyage for the discovery of a route to the South Sea should be made. Smith's enemies pushed the task on him, hoping he would not be so fortunate as to come back alive as he had been on the voyage up the Chickahominy. A small shallop was fitted up and, taking fourteen men with him, Smith accompanied the *Phoenix* as far as Point Comfort. From there he turned northward into Chesapeake Bay. If our story were about Smith instead of the Indian Princess, I would tell you of the many adventures that befell him during the next three months; how he crossed to the Eastern Shore and there met the Laughing King of Accomacke, who, many years later, proved himself to be a true friend of the English; how he explored the York and Potomac Rivers and met an Indian named Japazaws, who afterwards played an important part in the life of the Princess; how he nearly died from a wound made by a sting-ray fish, and how, at one time, he and his crew nearly starved. But we shall have to pass over these adventures and go back to Jamestown.

Things had gone badly there during the summer. Smith had

no sooner left than Ratcliffe commenced to carry things with a high hand. Because of his position, he took possession of the best of the provisions and set them aside for his private use. He paid no attention to the remonstrances of Master Scrivener and Master Hunt. Indeed, Sicklemore was the only one who could restrain him. The two men had evidently had dealings in the past, but both refused to speak if any questions were asked. During July chills and fever again broke out, and many colonists died; fatalities were especially heavy among those who had come on the *Phoenix* and had not become accustomed to the Virginia climate. Master Scrivener was desperately ill. Master Hunt attempted to care for him, but it was too much for his feeble strength, and before the summer was over, his body was laid to rest in the Virginia he loved. Ratcliffe insisted that the men who were able to work spend their time preparing clapboards for a governor's palace he proposed to build about a quarter of a mile east of the fort. On account of this, the working of the corn was neglected, and a slender harvest resulted.

Smith and his companions returned early in the fall. Ratcliffe had thoroughly disgusted all the colonists, so they had arrested him and placed Master Scrivener in charge. He immediately took the provisions Ratcliffe had appropriated and distributed them among the colonists. He ordered the work on the palace stopped. A Council meeting was held. Smith was unanimously elected president till they should hear from the Company, and he set energetically to work. The stockade had not been replaced since the fire, and a new one was built at once. This time it enclosed three acres of ground and was "five-square," or pentagonal in shape. The few buildings that had been built in the spring were of sappy timber that had warped during the summer, so they needed repairing. The storehouse was reroofed so as to be ready for the supplies they hoped would come in the next vessel from England. The church was repaired, so morning and evening prayers and Sunday services, which had been suspended after Master Hunt's death, could be resumed. Each

Sunday the colonists, by turns, read a homily. Now, for the first time, it looked as if the colony were permanently settled.

In October a sail was sighted. The whole place was at once thrown into confusion. Hope and fear ran high. Suddenly a shout was raised, for the lookout had called that it was an English ship. She soon dropped anchor near the shore and a boat was lowered. In it were Newport and a number of gentlemen. The Council members stood together to receive them. "Gentlemen," said Newport, "allow me to make you acquainted with Captain Peter Winne and Captain Richard Waldo, two gentlemen whom the king has appointed to a place on the Council; also, Master Francis West, brother to my Lord la Warre."

The greetings were being acknowledged in a formal way, when a cheer broke from the men standing behind the Councilors. "A farthingale! A farthingale!" The boat had returned to the ship and was taking off a second load of passengers. At that moment a woman was seen to get into the boat, and presently another followed.

Captain Newport smiled. "I bring seventy colonists," he explained, "and among them are a lady and her maid." Then, as the boat came up to the shore—"Gentlemen of the Council, let me bring to your acquaintance Master Thomas Forest and his wife, Mistress Forest; also, Anne Burras, her maid." The welcome was enthusiastic. It was nearly two years since these men had laid eyes on one of their countrywomen.

Suddenly one of the young laborers pushed his way to the front, cap in hand. "Dost remember me, Mistress Anne?"

"La! John Laydon!" she exclaimed. "To think of seeing you here! And Sam Collier, and Dick Belfield too!" as those two appeared. "I' faith, the New World will not be so dull after all."

The whole company was soon on shore. Among its number were eight Poles and Dutchmen who had been sent to teach the colonists how to make glass, tar, pitch and soap ashes. The best house in the palisade was turned over to Mistress Forest and her maid. Newport grudgingly turned over to Smith the package

of letters and instructions from the Company. He took them
aside to examine at his leisure. Toward evening he walked out
into the stockade and called to Master Percy, "Wouldst like to
walk with me, George?"

"Gay and gladly, Jack," responded Percy.

They set out at a rapid pace over the neck of land, toward
the forest. It was only after they were under the giant cedars
and oaks that Smith spoke. " 'Twould have been better had we
planted our colony in a spot like this," he said. "The low, marshy
ground suffocates me, and certes, it breeds fever for us all."

"Didst bring me out here to discuss moving the town, John?"
inquired Percy a little mischievously.

"Nay, nay, George," replied Smith, smiling faintly, " 'twas
but a fleeting thought." He paused a moment. "The Council has
appointed me president of the colony for the next year." Percy
gave an exclamation of pleasure. "Yes," continued Smith, "I am
thankful to God that He has raised me, once a poor, friendless
boy, to such a high estate as president of one of His Majesty's
colonies." There was another pause before he spoke again. "They
are much displeased at the cargoes the ships have borne home,
and at the reports of our voyages of discovery. That load of
gilded dirt proved to be useless. 'Tis evident that scamp Wingfield and Newport carried evil tales to them. They say that
an we do not send back to them a lump of true gold or discover
a passage to the South Sea or the lost Roanoke colonists, we are
to remain as banished men. What do they expect of us?" he
suddenly burst out. "Half our company is dead long since, and
they wish the living to care for the sick and dying as well as do
the work of twice our number. Were one of them to come
hither and see for himself how we have to fight Indians and
famine, mayhap they would not so grandly demand a lump of
gold. As to that passage to the South Sea," he went on more
quietly, "I have most surely endeavored to find that, and I opine
that it is impossible. Virginia is far greater than we thought at
first, and we shall have to cross high mountains and mighty plains
ere we reach the ocean again."

"Is that the whole of the Company's instructions?" asked Percy.

"One thing more," replied Smith, "the Company instructs that Powhatan be crowned."

"What reason in that?" demanded Percy in astonishment.

"Newport claims he has definite information that gold is to be found in the country of the Monacans, and mayhap 'twould tickle Powhatan's vanity to crown him so he would go against the Monacans with us. I tell you, George, that 'twill be the confusion of us all so they insist on carrying out that silly scheme."

All these matters were taken up by the Council the following morning. Ratcliffe and Newport plainly showed amusement and triumph as the secretary read the severe words of the Company. After the letters were read, Smith spoke: "The orders are absurd, gentlemen. We have traveled upward of three thousand miles in search of the South Sea and the Roanoke colonists. And Newport"—sharply turning toward that gentleman—"methinks that after towing home a load of dirt, you would hesitate again to stir up that craze."

Newport sprang to his feet and turned his back on Smith as he faced the other members. "I have information on which I can rely that gold is to be found in the country of the Monacans. Shall we let savages make sling shot of golden pebbles we should claim?"

"Nay, nay!" shouted Ratcliffe.

"Silence!" thundered Smith. "Captain Newport, dost wish to urge us to fight friendly Indians? Methinks we have trouble enow nearer home. As for the matter of crowning Powhatan, 'tis naught but folly. The savage thinks highly of himself now. Were we to tickle his vanity further, methinks 'twould make him but the harder to deal with."

"The orders of the Company are positive," said Newport, addressing the ceiling. "They have sent to Powhatan a robe and a crown, a bed and bedstead and a basin and ewer. These are to be given to him, and he is to be crowned king."

"And mayhap, after Powhatan knows the meaning of luxuries, 'twill take more than *one* box of beads and other gauds to buy four bushels of corn," retorted Smith.

Newport sprang to his feet with a snarl of rage, his hand on his sword. Smith also rose, but Master West stepped between the two angry men. " 'Tis not meet for Christian men to be athirst for the blood of one another. Put up your sword, Captain Newport, and we will settle the matter peaceably."

"It seems to me," remarked Captain Winne, "that 'tis not for us to discuss the wisdom of the matter. 'Tis our duty to endeavor to carry out the instructions of the Company. If haply the lump of gold is impossible, leastways we can crown the heathen king."

"Mayhap 'twill not do so great harm as Captain Smith fears," suggested Master West. "We can at least send Powhatan a message that we have presents for him."

"There is none so fit to take that message as Captain Smith," said Ratcliffe, who never lost an opportunity to send Smith into enemy country.

"I shall undertake the errand, so it meets with the pleasure of the Council," Smith returned quietly.

Captain Waldo shot a surprised glance at Ratcliffe. "So there's any danger in the mission, 'twill be my pleasure to accompany Captain Smith."

"Have with you, friend," heartily echoed Winne.

" 'Tis not a dangerous errand, gentlemen," said Smith, "but belike you would take interest in our savage neighbors, so I'll gladly include you in the party."

A busy scene met the eyes of the councilors as they stepped out of the door. Two boys were usually appointed to prepare the food for the colony in a common kettle. Now there was quite a crowd gathered round the fire. In the midst was Anne Burras, vigorously superintending the preparations. Every man or boy in the colony who had nothing else to do was in the crowd, eager to help.

"Canst lay the table, Master Laydon?" asked Anne as she

bent over the boiling pot to give it another stir. "The soup is well nigh ready."

"There's marchpane enow for us all," Laydon whispered to Sam Collier.

"Verily, the presence of a woman makes a great difference," whispered Percy to Smith as they watched the glowing cheeks of the girl, surrounded by lads eager to do her bidding.

"The noon meal is ready, gentles," called the girl in her bright, strong voice. "Stand back, boys, till your betters be served."

"Good morrow, Mistress Anne, and how is your mistress today?" asked Percy.

"She is still abed, sir," said Anne with a curtsey. "She stood the voyage but poorly."

Two days later Smith and several other colonists set out to invite Powhatan to the coronation ceremonies. "So you see the little princess," said Percy as he bade the group good-by, "tell her 'tis many, many moons since we have seen her bright face." A few moments later the party was lost to sight as it passed rapidly through the woods in the direction of the York River, on the bank of which was Powhatan's home.

CHAPTER IX

The Coronation

Just before sunset the colonists arrived at Weromocomoco. A large number of Indians came out to welcome them. In answer to a request to see the chief, the Englishmen were told that he was away from home but would return at the rising of the sun. Smith refused an urgent invitation to stay in the village, and the party remained in a field near the woods.

"Where does the little princess hide herself, Captain Smith?" inquired Francis West. "We have heard naught but 'Princess Pocahontas' since our arrival, and 'tis time we saw her. Is it the scarcity of women that calls your attention to her, or is she truly so charming?"

"She is the only squaw of any looks whom I have seen," replied Smith. "But i' faith, there are many Englishwomen worse favored than she."

"Judging from current accounts," broke in Captain Waldo, "the whole colony is like to worship the maiden."

"And with good reason!" exclaimed Sam Collier. "More than once she has kept us from hunger, and you have heard how she preserved the life of my master. 'Twould be ingrate of us did we not love her."

"Hast mermaids in these woods?" suddenly demanded West as a faint singing became audible. All turned in the direction of the village, where they could just discern in the dusk forms darting between the trees.

"Have an eye for your arms, men," cautioned Smith. " 'Tis

a sad fact that our neighbors are ofttimes tricky." He continued to peer anxiously into the dusk. Suddenly he laughed uproariously. " 'Tis a masque after the Virginia manner, with which they will amuse us."

A band of girls sprang from the woods and ran toward the Englishmen. The upper parts of their bodies were bare and dashed with puccoon. All wore necklaces and bracelets of beads and shells, and had bucks' horns fastened to their foreheads. Pocahontas was in the lead. There was an otter skin at her waist and another on her arm. Over her shoulder was a quiver filled with arrows and she carried a bow in her hand. Singing all the while, the girls formed a ring around the white men.

"Methinks 'twould be more fit to greet this company with a harp rather than a matchlock," whispered West to Smith. "By my honor! Who is the modern Diana?" he exclaimed as Pocahontas faced him for the first time.

"The princess," replied Smith quietly.

"Truly she would grace Whitehall," murmured West.

From the low notes with which the song had begun, the voices now became more shrill and high. Suddenly all the singers ceased save Pocahontas, who carried on the strange air alone. Faster and faster they whirled around, now with a full chorus and now with only a single voice. All at once, with a shrill cry, they darted toward the trees and changed from woodland elfs to shy brown maidens.

"Ho, ho!" roared West in delight. "How I wish my English Mary could have seen the Virginia princess."

Presently Pocahontas advanced quietly from the woods and walked toward Smith. "Captain," she said with the little lisp that accompanied all her words, "supper is ready an you care to eat."

She led the party to a wigwam, and there the Indian girls, divested of their antlers, served the visitors a typical Indian feast, with food piled high on wooden trenchers. West was delighted and kept up a continual flow of songs and jokes. "Body o' me!" he exclaimed. "I am athirst." Pocahontas handed him a gourd of pohickory. West caught her hand and attempted to pull her down beside him. "I trow that one taste of Your Highness's lips would quench my thirst better than a goblet of heathen liquor."

As the girl struggled to free herself, West found Smith standing over him, his eyes flashing and sword in hand. "Captain West, you are not dealing with a serving maid in Windsor!"

"I cry your pardon!" exclaimed West. "And Your Highness" —as he rose and made a profound bow— "so you'll hold me excused, the offense will not be repeated."

The newcomers were astonished at Smith's preparations for the night. Since the ground was damp, he made a huge fire. When it had burned long enough to dry the ground under it, the logs were dragged to another spot. The warm spot was swept with a dogwood branch to remove any embers. Mats, supplied by the Indians, were spread over the spot. Other mats were hung in the trees as screens to break the wind. When the wind shifted during the night, Smith roused his companions and had them move the fire again to make another warm bed for themselves.

In the morning they found Powhatan sitting by a fire, surrounded by warriors. He listened gravely to Smith's invitation to visit Jamestown, and a dry smile flitted over his face at the mention of the coronation. "If your king has sent me presents," he said dryly, "I also am a king and he must come to me. Eight days will I remain here. I will not come to your fort, neither will I bite at such a bait."

Smith tried to persuade him, saying that Newport would join him in fighting the Monacans. "I can avenge my own injuries," retorted Powhatan, "and as for any relation from my people concerning salt waters beyond the mountains, they are false."

Seeing that talk was useless, the colonists returned to Jamestown and delivered Powhatan's message to Newport. " 'Tis my rede that the silly matter had best be dropped," Smith told him.

"The orders of the Company must be carried out," retorted Newport.

" 'Tis plain you are ever more ready to obey the savages than to compel them to obey you," said Smith coldly. "Go an you will. I stay here."

A large party headed by Newport left for Weromocomoco. Powhatan received the newcomers graciously and in the presence of a large crowd the ceremony began. Powhatan was pleased with his presents and condescendingly put on the scarlet cloak. Newport directed him to kneel so that the crown could be placed on his head. Powhatan flatly refused. " 'Tis unkingly to bend the knee."

He turned a deaf ear to all their persuasions, and finally Newport, with the aid of some of the others, was compelled to try leaning on his shoulders till he stooped enough to allow the crown to be placed on his head. At that moment a volley was fired. Powhatan sprang aside in fear. But when he saw that no harm was meant, in a very dignified manner he presented Newport with his robe of raccoon skins and a pair of beaded moccasins. "For my brother, the King of England, with my complimental courtesy," he said.

"Has Powhatan any corn for his father?" inquired Newport in a soothing tone.

"My boys will carry it to the boat," replied Powhatan over his shoulder as he strode off into the forest.

When Newport reached the boat, he found seven bushels of wheat ears. Master West broke into a loud laugh, but at the sight of Newport's face, he prudently controlled his mirth.

When Newport reached Jamestown, he insisted on taking a party of one hundred and twenty chosen men up the James into the Monacan country in search of gold. When he returned, half the party was sick and all of its members were complaining, discontented and sullen. "Didst bring any corn?" Smith demanded, "or was the boat too full of gold?"

"The Monacan dogs had hid their gold so well that it could not be found," replied Newport.

"Mayhap you learned a good lesson," said Smith shortly, "and will run after no more marsh fires, but will trust to steady labor."

"I will take a larger force and more arms and compel it from them."

"By my faith, you shall not!" shouted Smith angrily. " 'Tis

all one as murder to go against friendly Indians. There are overly many masters in this town now."

"We'll see about that, my little gamecock!" retorted Newport. "I'm here to carry out the commands of the Company."

Before the words were well out of his mouth, Smith had seized him by the doublet and, with a dextrous twist of the foot, had thrown him on the ground. "One more word and I'll send the ship home without you and keep you here for a year to learn to speak of your own inconvenience."

"Dost need any help, Captain?" said Powell, running up. "Make him cry *peccavi!*"

"So I let you up, Newport, will you cease this idle talk and go about the preparations to return home?"

"Yea," replied Newport sullenly.

"George," said Smith to Percy not long before the departure of the ship, "you are a ready writer. Wouldst like to read the letter I've writ in answer to the complaints of the honorables?"

"Right gladly," answered Percy.

"I shall not burden you with it all. I first told them 'twas my rede that the time spent on a search for gold or for the South Sea, or the Roanoke colonists had best be put on something else. But listen to this: 'From your ship we had not provision in victuals worth twenty pound, and we are more than two hundred to live upon this. The sailors daily make good cheer, but our diet is a little meal and water and not sufficient of that. Though there be fish in the sea, fowls in the air and beasts in the woods, their bounds are so large, they so wild, and we so weak and ignorant, we cannot much trouble them. Captain Newport we much suspect to be the author of inventions. Now that you should know, I have made you as great a discovery as he, for less charge. I am sending you a map of the Bay and rivers, with an annexed relation of the nations that inhabit them. Also I am sending two barrels of stones, such as I take to be good iron ore at the least. The soldiers say many of your officers maintain their families out of that you send us and that Newport has a hundred pounds a year for carrying news.'"

"You'd best remember," broke in Percy hastily, "that Newport and Wingfield will be on the spot and will press their opinions on the Company."

"Aye, and I've given our opinion of some of these gentlemen," said Smith dryly, continuing to read: " 'Captain Ratcliffe is a poor counterfeit impostor, sometimes called Sicklemore. I am sending him home, lest the colony should cut his throat. What he is, everyone can tell you. If he and Archer return again, they are sufficient to keep us always in factions. When you send again, I intreat you rather to send but thirty carpenters, husbandmen, gardeners, fishermen, blacksmiths, masons and diggers-up of trees and roots, well provided, than a thousand of such as we have. Except we be able both to lodge them and feed them, the most will consume necessaries before they can be made good for anything. Please consider Captain Newport so long staying here; (notwithstanding his boasting to leave us victuals for twelve months) we were constrained to give him three hogsheads of that to victual him homeward. I humbly intreat you hereafter, let us know what we should receive and not stand to the sailor's courtesy to leave us what they please. These are the causes that have kept us in Virginia, from laying such a foundation, that ere this might have given much better content and satisfaction. As yet you must not look for any profitable returns. So I humbly rest.' Is it plain enow, George?" he asked with some anxiety.

" 'Twill greatly displease some of them," said Percy anxiously, but they sealed the letter and delivered it to Newport. It came duly into the hands of the Company in London and became known there as Smith's "rude answer."

Later John Laydon came to Smith and diffidently asked, "May I have a private word with you, Captain?" They walked a little way off from the others. "What's troubling you, my lad?" Smith asked kindly.

The young fellow stood with his head hung down, in the greatest embarrassment, " 'Tis about Mistress Anne," he finally stammered.

Smith turned his head to hide his smile. "And what about her?"

"We be old friends," Laydon finally explained. "In the old

days in England I would fain have been her bachelor, but she did say me nay. To anger her, I paid my court to another lass. She knew then I was but fooling, but now she pretends to think I am troth plight to another lass."

"So you would fain be her bachelor still?" asked Smith.

"An she will have me," replied Laydon. "But all the other lads are paying court to her, and Master Sicklemore is also giving her compliments. Her head is turned with a gentleman's attention."

"We'll have none of that," said Smith sternly. "An Sicklemore means to deal honestly by the girl, well and good, but we'll have no improper flirting."

" 'Tis that I wished to speak of," said Laydon in a relieved tone. "I thought mayhap you would speak to Master Sicklemore. And could you ask Mistress Anne if she really means to say me nay or is just teasing me, I'll be humbly grateful."

"You're a good lad, John," said Smith kindly. "I'll try to unravel this coil and set the matter right."

They returned to the fort, the honest carpenter having a lighter heart than he had had since his old sweetheart had re-entered his life.

CHAPTER X

The Princess Gives a Warning

So well did Master Smith succeed in dealing with Anne that presently the colonists were preparing for a wedding. The ceremony was hurried on account of Mistress Forest, whose health was rapidly failing; the Council did not wish the girl to be left without a protector. Also, they wished the chaplain on Newport's boat to perform the ceremony.

Laydon's friends helped him to build a new house for his bride, while Smith and Scrivener made necessary repairs on the church. Anne herself took the lead in all the preparations. She sent for Pocahontas to be a bridesmaid. The Indian girl seemed pleased at the invitation, but neither Smith nor Anne could induce her to take part. The first English wedding in the new land was graced by all due honors and proper courtesy. The best wines and sweetmeats the colony could afford were set out. All donned their best clothes, and the slashed doublets of silk and velvet looked strangely out of place amid the forest surroundings. Francis West stood up with the groom, and Master Percy gave the bride away and was the first to kiss her. An account of the wedding that went back to England said: "We saw them bedded and gave them the caudle, but as we had no bridesmaids, we could not throw the stocking."

While Newport had been away on his expedition against the Monacans, Smith had begun on a plan to reorganize the colony so it could provide more necessities for itself. Even his best friends seemed somewhat set back by this new order of

73

things, but Smith would not listen to them, though he was good-humored about it. " 'Tis only meet for the Council to have some task to perform, as well as the rest of the colony. I propose to scheme work for all."

He sent Percy with the Poles and some of the English colonists to the far side of the neck of land, about a mile from the fort, to set up a glasshouse. Waldo and Winne and their associates started in to learn how to obtain tar, pitch and potash from the forest trees. Smith took the hardest task for himself. With a band of thirty newcomers he went about five miles down the river. They camped out in the woods while he taught them how to cut down trees and to make clapboards and wainscoating. He managed to infuse them with a spirit of friendly rivalry, so they worked willingly at this unaccustomed task. It was a happy group that gathered around the camp fire each evening.

"Captain," asked one of the group, "how happens it you are so skilled at tasks not befitting a soldier?"

"This is a hard country, my lad," replied Smith soberly. "So we do not conquer it, it will conquer us."

"My master has not always been so skilled as now," explained Sam Collier. "Do you mind the time you went fishing in the Bay, Captain?" he added mischievously.

Smith gave him a playful cuff. "Have done, boy!"

"Ho!" roared Master West. "I smell a good tale. Out with it, Sam! I'll protect you."

Sam prudently moved out of Smith's reach. " 'Twas when we were exploring the Bay. Hundreds of fish were all around us, sticking their snouts up out of the water. The captain told us to dip them out with the frying pan." He broke off.

"Well," West persisted. "What happened next?"

"Nothing," said Sam dryly.

Smith joined in the general shout of laughter. "I' faith, that time I learned a frying pan is not a good instrument to catch fish with."

In spite of the high morale, blisters were raised on tender palms by the hard labor and it was not uncommon to hear frequent oaths. Smith soon devised a plan to put a stop to this. He proposed a game of forfeits, the penalty to be set by vote. In glee, the men started the next day to number the oaths. The smiles left the faces of some when it was decided that the penalty was to be a cup of water poured down the sleeve of each culprit for every oath heard.

The first lot fell on John Russell. " 'Tis unfair to pick on me because I'm fat," he complained good-naturedly as he was being dragged forward. Man after man took his punishment, but a wet sleeve on a cold night was a poor bedfellow, and they soon decided oaths were not worth it.

" 'Tis good to see my master enjoying himself again," said Sam to Master West. "He was that harried by Master Ratcliffe and Master Archer, he all but forgot how to smile."

When this little group returned to Jamestown, the smile quickly faded from Smith's face. Those left in charge there had little to show for their labors.

" 'Tis but a taste of pitch, tar and glass we have ready to send back with Newport," Smith complained to West. "Percy failed me. He is so set on the idea 'tis the duty of the Company to supply everything, he neglects to do what he can. I tell you, do we not find commodities here for trade, this colony cannot live."

Not long after Newport left, disaster again threatened. Supplies on hand were barely sufficient to feed the two hundred men he had left there till spring. The corn, raised the previous summer, had been carefully gathered and stored in hogsheads. With the little procured from the Indians, Smith hoped they had food to last till spring. He sent Sam Collier to the storehouse to open a hogshead.

The boy came rushing out with white, scared lips. "Master," he shouted, "the corn is gone!"

"Gone?" exclaimed Smith. "What mean you, boy?"

"The rats have eaten it. There's scarce a grain left."

Smith and other members of the Council hastened to the storehouse and found the bad news only too true. A swarm of rats scurried out of sight at the men's approach, leaving everything littered with empty hulls of corn. It was a very sober group of men. Smith did not speak till he had examined every hogshead to see what was left. "The supply will scarce hold out a month," he said grimly, "and Powhatan has shown himself to be very sour and sullen of late."

"Dost fear he will withhold corn from us in this extremity?" asked Master West anxiously.

"Despite his professions of friendship, I fear me Powhatan would rejoice to see us starve."

"Are there not other tribes who would supply us?" asked Master Winne.

"They are all under Powhatan's authority," answered Percy. "Our only hope is the princess."

" 'Tis but a slender hope," said Smith. "We had best man the boats and set out for Weromocomoco. An the old Indian does not produce the corn, we must e'en capture him, and then, forsooth, the corn will be forthcoming."

"Nemattanow wishes to speak with you, sir," said Sam, coming up at this moment.

Later Smith returned to the men who were still in the storehouse. " 'Tis a very fortunate occurrence. Powhatan has sent asking if we cannot send men to build him a house. Also, he says he has corn to exchange for swords and guns."

"Humph!" exclaimed Master West, "a modest request, i' faith."

"At any rate, we'll have that corn," said Smith positively. "Mayhap we had best send some of those lazy Dutchmen overland to build the house, and the others of us can go by boat."

Quite a large force of colonists started down the James. They sailed in the pinnace and took with them two smaller barges. Captain Winne was left in charge at Jamestown. As they passed the mouth of Pagan River, Sasenticum, the Werowance of the Warrascoyacks, hailed the boat. "I wish a word with Captain Smith," he called.

"Come aboard!" was the hearty reply, for this Indian had shown himself to be friendly.

"You go to Powhatan for corn, is it not so?" Sasenticum asked. "You will find he will use you kindly, but trust him not. He does but send for you to cut your throats. And most of all, let him not have opportunity to seize your guns." After the friendly Indian had left, Smith repeated the message to Percy. "I thanked him for his good counsel, but 'twas not needed. 'Tis not my nature to trust these savages."

They anchored that night at Kecoughtan. The next morning was so cold and stormy and the river so full of ice that Smith deemed it unwise to proceed. They were compelled to remain there for a week. Here Smith spent his second Christmas, feasting on oysters, wild fowl and venison, but no wheat or corn. It was the middle of January before they came in sight of Weromo-comoco. The colonists landed, and taking possession of the first vacant wigwam they saw, they sent Powhatan word that they had arrived. He sent plenty of provisions for the night, with the message that he would see them in the morning.

When he appeared, Smith saw instantly a change in the chief's manner. Now there was no "complimental courtesy" for his white brothers. "When are you going away?" demanded Powhatan in the midst of Smith's remarks of greeting. "If you have come for corn, you will be disappointed, for my people have not enough for themselves. Mayhap they might exchange a very little for swords."

"I should like to mind you," said Smith angrily, "that we are come at your invitation and because you said you had corn to sell."

Powhatan broke into a grim laugh. "I was but fooling. My people will sell corn for swords. Only put out the matches of your guns, for they so affright my poor people they will not bring the corn."

Smith ignored the remark about the matches and very firmly replied, "We have no swords to exchange for corn, but here are the hen and cock and the grindstone you asked for."

"Captain Smith, have I not been a friend to the white men? Now, I wish to spend the winter of my days in quiet and not continually be in fear of trouble. You are a rash youth, but I wish to be friends with you. The corn shall be delivered, but let your people show themselves to be friendly also, and come for it unarmed."

The appeal might have touched Captain Smith had he not seen warriors gathering outside the wigwam. Powhatan noticed his roving eyes and fled, leaving a woman who endeavored to attract Smith's attention. Suddenly Smith broke away from her and rushed out of the wigwam, shooting his pistol. The Indians tumbled over each other in their efforts to get out of the way. To smooth over the appearance of so many warriors, Powhatan reappeared and said the corn had been brought. An exchange was soon made.

"Now let my white brothers stack their guns, and my people will guard them while the corn is being put on the boat," suggested Powhatan with a benevolent smile.

"Nay, nay," Smith replied. "Your people shall load the boat while the white men guard their own arms." Powhatan stood too much in awe of his warlike visitor to protest.

By the time the boat was loaded, the tide had turned, and Smith realized he would be compelled to spend the night there.

"Whist, Captain Smith, what is that?" West inquired suddenly.

"I heard naught," replied Smith.

"I saw something move behind those trees yonder."

With his sword in hand, Smith advanced in the direction indicated, when suddenly, and to his great surprise, Pocahontas stepped from behind a large tree and stood in the shadow, awaiting his approach. "What is it, child?" asked Smith.

The girl turned her face toward him, and he could see that it was tearstained. "Mayhap 'tis wrong to tell you, but my father is planning your destruction this night."

"How is that, little one?"

"Presently boys will come bearing you a great feast. Whilst you are eating, warriors will come to kill you. I have tried to dissuade my father"—she commenced to sob—"but he will not listen."

"We will be on guard, child," replied Smith. "Take this, little maid"—handing her a chain he drew out of his frieze jerkin.

"I cannot take it. My father would know where I received it, and he would kill me. Be on your guard." Her voice broke again. "Only do not hurt my people."

"God bless you, Matoaca," Smith whispered gently, placing his hand on her bowed head. Impulsively she caught his hand in both of hers for a moment and then flitted back into the forest.

Smith returned to his companions and told them what he had heard. " 'Tis a wondrous kind heart she has," he murmured. "God bless her," said Percy, and "Amen," echoed West, while the rest looked up in surprise to hear the break in his voice.

Soon, as Pocahontas had said, boys appeared bearing a bountiful feast. "Here, you," exclaimed Smith, seizing one of the boys by the arm, "taste this"—pointing to a large trencher of venison. When the boy obeyed, he forced him to taste every other article of food also. "I did fear Powhatan would take a more subtle way of dealing with us," he said as the boys withdrew.

All night long the boys were coming and going, but since they found white men on their guard, no attack was made. In the morning Smith sailed up the river to the residence of Opechancanough, Powhatan's brother, who had promised corn also.

Smith and his party were led into a wigwam and began bartering for corn, when one of the men called out that they had been betrayed. Fully seven hundred armed warriors surrounded them. Instantly Smith seized the chief by the hair and, pressing his pistol against the savage's breast, dragged him out of the wigwam. The Indians were terror-stricken and instantly threw down their arms and brought out the corn.

"The reason I bear your insolence now for so long," Smith sternly told Opechancanough, "is that I made a vow to God to be your friend. So I keep this vow, God will help me and you cannot hurt me. You have broken all friendship by your actions.

You promised to load my ship with corn, and so you shall or I shall load it with your dead bodies. An you bring the corn, I shall mind me how you saved my life when I was in your power, and shall be your friend forever."

Now, having a full load of corn, Smith sailed back to Jamestown. Sad news greeted him. Master Scrivener and Master Waldo had gone to an island down the river where the hogs had been placed to find pasture for themselves. A sudden storm had come up, the boat had capsized and they had been drowned. "More good friends gone," Smith told Percy as the volley customary for Council members was fired over the graves.

Chapter XI

Exit Captain Smith

The colony now entered upon six months of unprecedented prosperity. The ringleaders of the mutinous party had left and Smith found little opposition to his wise rule. On account of his expedition, there was a supply of corn sufficient to last till the new crop could be harvested. Now that danger of starvation was over, the gentlemen settled themselves down for a life of ease. This Smith would not allow. He assembled the whole colony and made a formal speech:

"You see now, my countrymen, by grace of the London Company, that power rests wholly in myself. You must obey this for law: He that will not work shall not eat. Though you presume authority is but a shadow, and that I dare not touch the lives of any, except my own must answer for it, yet he that offends, let him surely expect due punishment. Dream no longer of a vain hope from Powhatan, or that I will longer forbear to force you from your idleness or punish you if you rail. I protest by that God that made me, since necessity has no power to force you to gather for yourselves, that you shall not only gather for yourselves, but also for those that are sick. On the morrow, after prayers, from ten till four o'clock, every well man must work."

The laborers were much amused at this turn of events. John Laydon gleefully reported to Anne, "The captain has set up a public list, for all to see, of each man's deserts and the amount of work he does each day."

George Percy made a feeble attempt to dissuade Smith from this new program. " 'Tis still winter and many tasks had best wait till spring."

"I can find tasks for all," replied Smith impatiently. "I tell you, George, we must learn to provision ourselves off the land. That lazy Indian who was taken prisoner last fall knows useful things, and I'll see to it he earns his keep."

The sturgeon were then running, and more were caught each day than could be eaten. Under the Indian's directions, the fish were first dried and then pounded to a paste. When mixed with sorrel and other herbs, this made a good food for the colonists to carry with them when they left Jamestown.

Others were sent out into the marshes to gather tockwogh roots. They made quite a fete of preparing these. A shallow pit was dug and filled with roots. They were well covered with dry oak leaves and ferns, and for twenty-four hours a hot fire was kept burning over the pit. Prepared in this way, the roots could be substituted for bread.

Master West was inclined to disparage it. "I tried them," he confided to Percy, "and they pickled and tormented my throat sorely."

"Mayhap 'twas a tough root and not cooked long enow," volunteered Sam. "True, 'tis not a very tasty dish, but 'tis better than no victuals at all."

A vast deal of work was accomplished that spring. A well was dug in the fort; twenty new dwellings were erected; a blockhouse was built at the beginning of the neck of land leading to the main, and another on Hog Island, as well as a fort on a rising piece of ground across the river. Also, forty acres of ground were cleared and prepared for planting corn.

One disturbance marred the peace of the spring months. Captain Winne, who had been left in command while Smith was away, was making his report and surprised Smith by asking, "Why didst send those Dutchmen for more arms?"

"What arms?" gasped Smith.

"The Dutchmen you sent to build the house for Powhatan

came, after you left, and said you had need of their arms, so they wanted new ones. They took more tools, also, and a shift of apparel."

Sam Collier, who seemed to get around among the men and learn the news, added to Smith's uneasiness. "Captain, they do say those cursed Dutchmen, Adam and Francis, got swords, pike heads, guns, shot, powder, and e'en that small forge."

"Didst learn who supplied them?"

"Nay, but I did discover they use the glasshouse for a rendezvous. Indians hide in the woods to carry away the commodities, so when Adam and Francis depart, their hands are empty."

"Captain Winne also said," remarked Smith, "that he found Adam roaming in the woods. When he taxed him, Adam excused himself by saying he was but gathering walnuts."

Sam made another report later. "They now say Adam is teaching the Indians to fire arms in the woods around the glasshouse, and that Francis has forged for them three hundred hatchets."

Smith at once set out for the glasshouse alone. He passed the new blockhouse and had just reached the woods on the other side of the neck of land, when Wowinchopunk suddenly sprang from behind a tree and grappled with him. Smith was so unprepared for the attack that the savage threw him into the water. But Smith had gotten a firm hold on his enemy and dragged him in, also. They struggled, each trying to drown the other, till Smith got the upper hand and drew his sword to cut the Indian's throat. Wowinchopunk set up such a howl for mercy that Smith carried him prisoner to Jamestown. He confessed he had been employed by the Dutchmen. He escaped, however, and he and his warriors lay in wait near the glasshouse thereafter to kill those who ventured too far.

With this exception, the days passed peaceably. Pocahontas again became a constant visitor, and frequently she brought Nantauquas with her. The boy, by his manly and dignified behavior, soon became as great a favorite as his sister, though Smith and Percy showed a strong partiality for the princess. It

was during this time that Percy commenced to teach Pocahontas
to read, and she amazed them all by her quickness at learning.

But this peace did not last, and during July there was the first
hint of trouble. Captain Samuel Argall, a buccaneer, was out on
a private trading expedition and stopped at Jamestown. He was
entertained in Smith's house. There were present also Percy,
West and Winne.

Argall drank heavily and soon became talkative. "Master
Percy, I bear you a message from your noble brother. He has
received the stones you sent and is having the great one set in a
ring. Also, since soon 'twill be your turn to be president of the
colony, he is sending a supply of new material for apparel."

"Didst bring it with you?" inquired Percy eagerly.

"Nay, 'twas better to let it come in a Company ship. But the
agent gave me a list. Certes, 'twill keep a tailor busy for a year!
Here!"—digging into his doublet. "Let me read. Material for five
suits to be made of chamlette, philizella, perpetuana, silk mockado
and fustian for a doublet with cloth breeches. There's lesser
fustian to line all suits, canvas for stiffening and taffeta for
facing. There is also broadcloth for a cloak."

At Percy's rapt expression, West gave a delighted burst of
laughter. Argall grinned and held up his hand. " 'Tis not yet done.
There are also stockings, garters, gloves, ribbon shoestrings,
twelve pairs of shoes, six boots *and*"—he paused impressively—
"four hats, two of silk with gold bands, a colored Dutch hat
edged in gold and a Monmouth cap." The men were listening
eagerly as Argall continued: "There are many sundries, including
combs and head brushes, and the list ends with Holland linen
and cambric for sheets, shirts, handkerchiefs and nightcaps. It
all adds up to near sixty pounds."

Abruptly he turned to Smith. "Wouldst like to have the latest
news from the Company, Captain?"

"So 'tis true," answered Smith shortly. He alone had seemed
unimpressed by the account of Percy's wardrobe.

"The barrel of stone you sent by Newport was good iron
ore and brought sixty-eight pounds from the East India Company."

"So!" said Smith in a pleased tone. "An the Company and others"—he shot a look at West and Percy—"would forget the great gilded hopes of the South Sea and settle for commodities that can be obtained here in Virginia, we could yet maintain a colony."

"The Company sees it not that way," replied Argall. "You are removed on account of hard dealing with the savages and not returning the ships profitably freighted."

" 'Tis a cruel charge against a man who ridiculed a cargo of yellow dirt and compels from the Indians only corn enow to keep life in the colony," said Smith bitterly.

"Aye, aye," said Argall. " 'Tis hard, but there's no help on't. The London Company is all done over. The Council is to be elected by the Company, not appointed by the king. So these other gentlemen are also displaced. My Lord la Warre is appointed Governor and Captain General, Sir Thomas Gates is Lieutenant Governor, Sir George Somers is Admiral and Sir Thomas Dale is High Marshal. They left England in May with a fleet of nine ships, and they bring five hundred settlers."

The news was indeed true. Newport and Ratcliffe had taken their revenge on Smith. The rough soldier who wrote "rude answers" to the Company was no match for smooth-tongued courtiers. It was August when the fleet arrived, and a sorry-looking fleet it was. While it was passing the Azores, a storm had risen and the ships had suffered greatly. One had been lost, and the *Sea Venture*, bearing Gates and Somers, had been driven to the Bermuda Islands. Lord Delaware was to follow in the spring. The remaining seven ships had reached Jamestown safely.

The old settlers stood on the shore and half bitterly watched the unloading of the vessels. In the first boat that came ashore were Ratcliffe, Archer and Martin. In the absence of the appointed officials, Ratcliffe claimed authority. His demands were curtly refused by Smith. "Doubtless your statements be true. Ne'ertheless I remain as president till proper officers arrive."

The town was in a ferment. Among the newcomers were unruly gallants banished to Virginia by their families. They upheld Ratcliffe's demand and spent their time roistering about the town. Smith was utterly disheartened. "I'm aweary of it all," he told Percy. "I'm in the black looks of the Company. I would fain leave all and return to England, but 'tis my duty to stay till the proper governor arrives."

At length, in order to quell the continued disturbance, he had to arrest Ratcliffe and Archer. Then, as the town was too small to accommodate so many people, he sent Martin down the river to Nansemond with a large number of settlers, and West up the river with another company. But West got into trouble with the Indians, and Smith had to go to help quiet the disturbance.

On the return trip a serious accident occurred. Smith was asleep, and in some unexplained way a spark fell on his powder pouch. There was a loud explosion. The flesh was torn from Smith's body and thigh, and his clothing was set on fire. With a scream of pain, he leaped overboard and sank immediately. Powell and Sam Collier followed, and as he rose, they caught him. He was lifted into the boat and lay there moaning in agony.

It was a solemn crowd of men who carried their wounded leader to his hut. Sam Collier was in tears. "My master was frying in his clothes," he told those who crowded around. An apothecary was called and did what he could for the suffering man, but it was little. All night long Smith tossed in delirium. In the morning he was rational and sent for Percy. "I'm done for, George," he said feebly.

"Not so, John. You're doing bravely this morn," answered Percy, trying to speak cheerfully, but his heart sank at the sight of his friend.

"I'm not like to mend with such tendance as I receive here. I'll have to give up."

"I've been trying to persuade him to return to England," said Powell, who had watched by his side all night.

"And leave the case to Ratcliffe? I'd liefer die."

"Softly, softly, friend," interposed Powell. "You'll bring on the fever again. 'Tis Master Percy's turn to be president. Leave it to him."

The ships were preparing to sail, so Smith's friends set about making ready for his departure. "George," said Smith the day before he was to leave. "The little princess—I could not leave without bidding her good-by."

"She'll be here before sunset," promised Percy.

Smith awoke from his sleep and found Pocahontas standing by him. "Child," he said gently, holding out his hand to her.

She caught it in both of hers and sank to her knees. "My Captain," she sobbed.

"I'm going away, little maid. Dost think you'll remember what I've tried to tell you?"

The girl raised her head. "Dost mean about your God?"

"Yea, little one. I could wish He were your God."

"He is! He is!" she exclaimed. "I pray no more to Okee."

"Thank God, Matoaca," said Smith, using her sacred name. For a few moments both were silent. Then Smith spoke again. "Dost love the white men, child?"

"Have I not shown I do?" she asked eagerly.

"Wilt ever help them, child? They are very weak and need care."

"Yea, yea, my Captain," she said as the tears ran down her cheeks.

" 'Tis time to leave, Pocahontas," said Percy. "Captain Smith is o'er weak and needs to rest against his long journey tomorrow."

Smith placed his hand on the girl's bowed head. "Farewell, child. God bless and keep thee."

Without speaking, she silently rose and left the room. "Her like is not to be found in Virginia," murmured Smith. Perhaps Percy was mistaken, but he thought there were tears in the soldier's eyes.

So Virginia lost her brave captain, without whose wise help and protection the colony would have perished before it took root.

CHAPTER XII

The Starving Time

When Smith left Virginia, there were in the colony five or six
hundred hogs, horses, sheep, goats and chickens. Surely, with
judicious management, the colonists had nothing to fear! But the
small cloud on the horizon was even then taking shape. The for
once ample supplies in the vessels had been ruined by salt water.
Smith's acres of corn, sufficient to supply two hundred people
over the winter, would not stretch to feed several hundred more.
Also, much of the growing crop had been eaten green by the
rowdy newcomers. And then an unthought-of terror showed its
ugly head. The new settlers had brought with them germs of
yellow fever and London Plague. Master Percy was early stricken,
and though he recovered, he was too weak to control the unruly
gallants.

As news of Smith's departure spread, the Indians began to
prove more troublesome. Wowinchopunk became bold and ag-
gressive. Powell and Waller were sent to capture him alive, but
finding it impossible, Powell rushed him and ran him through
with his sword. Also, some twenty of the settlers stole a large
supply of provisions and ran away with one of the vessels to
become buccaneers. Food was becoming scarce. In spite of
advice to the contrary, Ratcliffe insisted on going to Powhatan
to procure corn. The result was pathetic. The party reached
Weromocomoco and was kindly received. Presently a messenger
came from Powhatan. "The chief is afraid of the matches of
your guns," he said. "If you wish to trade, you must come as
friends and leave your arms behind."

"Do no such thing," counseled one of Smith's old soldiers. " 'Tis a snare."

"Your stupid captain is gone now," retorted Ratcliffe. " 'Tis for me to show a new method of dealing with the savages."

They stacked their guns and advanced. They had gone scarcely a score of yards before a pack of yelling Indians was upon them. The few colonists who had knives found it useless to attempt to defend themselves. One man, Jeffrey Shortridge, with a heavy stick, succeeded in beating off his assailant. He went backward towards the woods as fast as possible, when suddenly he felt himself jerked into an adjacent thicket, and at the same time a familar voice said, "Make no sound, Master Shortridge. So you are not discovered, the princess will see you safe."

The speaker was Henry Spelman, a twelve-year-old boy who had come in the last vessel and had been temporarily left with Powhatan. He was crouched close to the ground, in the middle of a thick, tangled growth of scrubby pines, vines and brush. Behind him was crouched the slender figure of a girl. Her dress of doeskin was torn with briers, and there were long scratches on her arms and hands. Her hair was in wild confusion. Her face was buried in her hands, and her shoulders were heaving with inaudible sobs. In answer to Shortridge's questioning look, Henry whispered, " 'Tis the princess. When she saw you so near, she said she would save you. Look!"—pointing to the open space where the fight was still raging—"is not that Captain Ratcliffe's head the red devil is holding up?"

"I tried to hinder it," moaned the girl. "My father sent me away, but I came back unbeknown to him. I will be but dead if he finds me."

The three stayed in the thicket till long after dark. Then, with the Indian maid in the lead, they crept to the banks of the York River. Shortridge swam across to take the news back to Jamestown. Henry had found that Pocahontas meant to set out that very night for the Potomac River, so he insisted on going with her.

This was the last news the white men had of the princess for a very long time. In order to understand the conditions at Jamestown when she was next seen there, we shall have to tell what befell the colonists during the next three years.

Plague and fever were still raging. Those that were well enough had all they could do to tend the sick and bury the dead. Supplies were now exhausted, and people were recklessly killing pigs, sheep and chickens. The settlers dared not venture beyond the blockhouse on account of the hostility of the Indians. The difficulty of procuring wood was so great that as houses were vacated by death, they would be torn down and used for fuel.

Anne Laydon, with her baby, Virginia, in her arms, was a ray of sunshine in the dismal scene. It was she who went from one stricken hut to another tending the sick and closing the eyes of the dead. As long as there was food to cook, she superintended the preparation. When the authorities were at last able to reduce things to order and put all provisions under guard so as to dole out daily rations, she cheerfully divided her share with little Jane Pierce, the blue-eyed, fair-haired daughter of Captain and Mistress William Pierce, both of whom lay at the point of death.

Anne stepped one morning from one of the houses, carrying a soiled blanket. She met Captain Powell hurrying down the path.

"Ah! Dame Laydon. How are the sick you tended last night?"

"Poor Master Forest died about day, but he was glad to go. Since my mistress died, he seemed not to care to live. I must needs wash his blanket. So many have traded their bed furniture to the Indians for a little corn, and now, in this bitter weather, they are like to freeze as they sleep."

"We have not had the like of this cold since we came to Virginia," answered Powell. "How is Mistress Pierce?"

"Doing better this morn. Had she the proper food, she might yet mend." She shook a limp apron. "I've e'en put all my starch into the kettle to piece out our victuals. How are those on your side of town?"

2u4-3

Bookworm & Silverfish Box 639, Wytheville, VA 24382

Ph: (276) 686-5813 | Fax: (276) 686-6636

5791320132

6U-5

(VA)(Native American)(Autog)
(Virginia)(Native American)(Autograph) Dixon, Margaret
Denny. THE PRINCESS OF THE OLD DOMINION. A
HISTORICAL NOVEL OF THE FIRST VIRGINIA COLONY. New
York, 1953, 120pp. First ed. Vg in good dust jacket (frayed
at top). Ex lib. Vanity Press. Inscribed and signed by
author. Our first copy.

HSY

$25.00

5791320132

"Three died last night and Master Percy is still very weak. I am now on my way to see Master Sicklemore. He is to go to Nansemond to try to get a little corn, and he wishes to see me ere he leaves."

Anne stepped closer to him and whispered, "Has he not been strange since the news came of poor Master Ratcliffe's murder? There must have been something untoward between them in the past."

"Tut, tut, woman!" rebuked Powell. "Gossip ill fits us now."

Sicklemore had a strange tale to tell: "Nat, should I not come back from this expedition, there is something you should know." His face flushed with passion and the next words came almost with a shriek. "I came here with murder in my heart! Many times I strove to find courage to run my sword through him, but God took the vengeance out of my hands!"

"Hold, man!" exclaimed Powell. "I take not your meaning. Catch your breath ere you go on."

Sicklemore made an effort to control himself. " 'Twas Ratcliffe. He was my half brother. My mother died and my father married again. His wife did not care for me as a mother should. Mayhap if she had, I might have been a better man. Ere John could plainly speak his words, he learned to tell lies on me. Then my father would punish me. Since I had the credit for misbehaving, I grew to be as bad as John made me out. When he became grown, John schemed to gain our father's property."

He walked nervously about the room several times before he went on. "Since God has taken vengeance, I hate him no longer. I was in London when I had news that my father had died just after his morning meal. Among his papers was a will leaving all to John. It was duly witnessed and the men swore to its truth. There was naught to do save accept it. John arrived only in time for the funeral. He soon sold the estate and left the country, after changing his name to Ratcliffe for his mother's family. I ever mistrusted that will. Four years after my father died, one of the witnesses was taken ill. Since he was an old friend, I had him tended. Ere he died, he told me the will was a forgery. At the point of a sword, John had forced him to sign and then lie about it. Also, John had bribed a servant to poison my father. Fifteen years later I pursued John to Virginia. Why I did not tell the story, I know not. Mayhap my years of poverty had made me craven, and John was in power here and had the ear of the Company. God took vengeance."

"Is there aught for me to do?" asked Powell uncomfortably.

Sicklemore seemed almost dazed. "I wanted you to know how I was tempted," he muttered. Powell silently turned away.

The situation of the colonists grew worse. Provisions were now exhausted and the few settlers left lived chiefly on nuts, roots and such animals and birds as they were able to snare. Tales of horror were a daily ocurrence. Sicklemore never returned, and later his mutilated body was found with its gaping mouth ironically stuffed with bread.

Sam Collier returned from a trip to one of his traps in the woods and ran gasping to Master Percy's hut. "Oh, sir," he burst out as soon as he could get his breath, "the man Newcomb, who lives in the woods on Back Creek, is eating his wife's body!"

"What mean you?" asked Percy in horror, and the others present shuddered.

"I smelled smoke and went about hunting for it. Newcomb had a fire with a boiling pot over it. I crept nearer and saw him go to a clump of brush and drag from it part of a body, frozen and salted. He cut off a piece and dropped it in the pot. I turned sick and crept away or ever he saw me. Oh, sir,"—and the boy sank trembling to the floor—"whatever are we coming to?"

"Methought when we punished those rascals for digging up that Indian and eating him, we would have no more cannibal feasts," said Powell. " 'Tis plain the end is near, when humans sink so low."

Spring found barely fifty people alive. On a beautiful afternoon Percy dragged himself out of doors and, after great effort, succeeded in getting beyond the fort. He lay down under a cedar tree and closed his eyes, wishing death would come to him in this quiet place. An unusual sound caused him to sit up and look down the river. He was so nearly gone that it required an effort to induce him to believe it was a sail he saw, and not a blur over his eyes. New strength came to him and he ran back to the town. His shouts brought to the bank of the river all who were able to stand. With tears streaming down their faces, they watched the approach of two weather-beaten vessels.

"Body o' me!" exclaimed William Pierce. " 'Tis Sir Thomas Gates and Sir George Somers, who were lost on the *Sea Venture*."

" 'Tis Captain Newport in the bow," added John Laydon.

"I care not who 'tis, so they bring us food," replied his wife. "Had they been a se'ennight later, naught but corpses would have welcomed them."

The men in the boat were looking toward the shore, amazement and consternation on their faces. In place of a healthy, thriving town, they looked at the wrecked palisade, with gates hanging on rusty, broken hinges. Beyond were a few dilapidated houses, and on the shore stood a pitiful handful of emaciated people.

" 'Tis a poor welcome we can give you," said Master Percy to Sir Thomas when the party had landed. "You are just in time to save what is left of the colony."

"God pity us all," replied Gates with concern in his voice. "We have suffered shipwreck ourselves and come hither expecting to be succored. Our provisions are scarce, but since you are starving, we can stay your hunger for the night. In the morning we shall better know what's to be done."

Chapter XIII

The Time of Delaware and Dale

The newcomers had a strange tale to tell. The hurricane blew the *Sea Venture* to Bermuda, where it was wrecked. Miraculously, the crew and passengers were saved. During the winter, under the direction of Sir George Somers, two small vessels, the *Patience* and the *Deliverance* were built from material salvaged from the *Sea Venture* and from wood obtained on the island. In late spring these little vessels, too scantily laden with food, set out for Jamestown.

A general meeting of all the men in the colony was called. " 'Tis necessary some plan be made at once," said Sir Thomas Gates. "I am come with a hundred souls and provisions but for a fortnight. How many are left living in the town, Master Percy?"

"About sixty, but some are so far gone they are not like to mend e'en though help has come."

"Dost think we are like to obtain corn from the Indians?" continued Sir Thomas.

"No," replied Newport, who had been in command of the *Sea Venture*. "Captain Martin gave me last night an account of the cruel massacre that took place when they last went to buy corn."

" 'Tis my rede, Sir Thomas," spoke Captain Powell, "that we had best set sail for England without delay, so you do not wish to be reduced to the sad case in which you find us."

"Nay, Nat," interrupted Captain Martin hastily, " 'tis too

good a land to give it over to red savages. Now that we have food for e'en a se'ennight and a fresh supply of powder, we can go against the Indians and compel corn from them."

"Why should we be able to compel corn now, when we could not six months agone?" asked William Pierce. "Sir Thomas, we are so close to death that all we beg is to go home to die."

"Sure, 'twould be a pity to turn back now, when so many lives have been sacrificed in the effort to people Virginia with Christians," Martin continued to urge. "Put some heart into them, Sir Thomas, and tell them 'tis not meet to cry quits now."

"Mayhap a year back 'twould have been best to risk all dangers," said Percy. "Now we have women and little children in our midst. I counsel a speedy return to England."

"Do you mind how Sir Richard Grenville's colony left Roanoke Island with Sir Francis Drake but a fortnight before Sir Richard returned with reinforcements?" insisted Martin. "Is England to add another to her list of failures in trying to people Virginia?"

"Has Sir Thomas bethought him what we shall do for provant on the voyage?" asked Sir George Somers.

"Our only hope is to head for Newfoundland. Once we reach there in safety, we can revictual the ships for the remainder of the voyage."

"Whate'er we do, 'tis doubtful whether we can preserve our lives," said one of the newcomers, Master John Rolfe. "Our best hope is to trust in God and the counsel of the majority."

"It goes against me to counsel retreat," said another newcomer, Sir George Yeardley, "but methinks these men, who have spent years in this land, are most fit to judge what aid we can get from the Indians. Without aid, we shall all die."

"We can expect naught from the savages save a tomahawk," said Powell. " 'Twas different so long as Smith and the princess were here. Now there's naught to do but leave so soon as may be."

"Is Captain Martin alone in counseling to remain?" asked Sir Thomas. There was a deep silence. "How long will we need to prepare to leave, Master Percy?"

"We must send word to Captain Davis and the guard at Point Comfort. So we send the pinnace downstream at once, he can be ready by tomorrow eve."

"How about those cursed Dutchmen?" asked Powell.

"Leave them to bide with Powhatan," growled Martin. "The old savage is crafty. He knows they betrayed us and will, when it suits their purpose, betray him. He can deal with them as he will."

"We'll burn this rotten old fort ere we go," said one of the young men bitterly.

"Silence!" said Sir Thomas sternly. "What arms we cannot take we'll e'en bury at the gate of the fort. All else shall be left as 'tis now."

At noon the following day the drums sounded for all to take their places in the boats. Sir Thomas remained on shore till all had embarked, to prevent the destruction of the town. A volley was fired and the *Patience* and the *Deliverance* sailed toward England.

"Let me turn my face toward the east," said Anne Laydon as she stood by her husband in the bow of one of the boats, holding her frail baby in her arms. "Mayhap 'twill make me feel nearer to England."

They stopped that night at Hog Island and started out again at daybreak. They had gone about five miles when the sails of the pinnace were seen coming rapidly toward them. As soon as the pinnace came within hailing distance of the advance vessel, its commander shouted through his hands, "News, news! My Lord la Warre has come!" There was a rush to the forward end of the vessel. "He reached Point Comfort yestere'en with a hundred and fifty settlers and victuals for a year. When he heard the bruit of your departure, he sent me with word for you to return to Jamestown and prepare for his arrival."

The news was received with varying degrees of joy and sorrow. "Praise the Lord!" shouted Martin. " 'Tis plain now that 'twas not God's will to abandon this land." That evening the colonists took possession again of their deserted homes.

"Jack," said Anne Laydon as they entered the little house he had built before their marriage, "since this is still to be our home, 'twould please me were you to help me redd it up a bit."

"That's my brave lass!" responded John fondly. "Virginia's as good a home as England so there's plenty to eat."

Lord Delaware arrived the next morning. Sir Thomas had everyone drawn up to receive him. A color bearer preceded him. As soon as Lord Delaware landed, he fell on his knees and offered a long and silent prayer. Then he rose and led the way to the church, where an impressive sermon was preached by the Reverend Richard Buck. Lord Delaware caused his commission from the king to be read and made a speech in which he mingled warning and encouragement. He proclaimed martial law and fixed definite hours of labor for all. He set the colonists to work cleaning the town and repairing the church. He had a walnut Communion table built and wainscoted the choir portion of the church with cedar planks. The windows were enlarged and fixed to be opened or shut, as the weather should dictate. New cedar pews were installed and there were two bells in the tower at the west end.

" 'Tis meet that God's house should receive first care," said Mistress Pierce in answer to a complaint from an unwilling gallant. " 'Tis passing sweet to have the sexton trim it with flowers for service."

Two services were held on Sunday, and morning and evening prayer each day. Lord Delaware set the example of attendance. At the ringing of the bell he appeared in full dress, accompanied by the lieutenant governor, the admiral, the vice admiral and the councilors and followed by halberd bearers wearing red cloaks. He himself sat in the choir, in a green-velvet chair, with a velvet cushion before him, on which he knelt.

"Alackaday!" whispered Powell to Martin as they watched this gorgeous procession file into the church. "This tender state of Virginia has not grown to such maturity as to be able to maintain a personage with such great attendance."

One of the newcomers was Madame West. " 'Tis my English

Mary," said Sir Francis West when he introduced her to Captain Martin. "You mind I spoke of her the time we were on York River and the princess danced for us."

"Where is the princess?" said Madame West. "Such glowing accounts have made me eager to see her."

"The little maid has not been seen for more than a year," answered Powell. "Mayhap she has forgotten us."

"She has not forgotten, I warrant," said West. " 'Tis not her fault these misfortunes have come upon the colony."

Under the rule of Lord Delaware a degree of prosperity settled on the colony. Unfortunately, this did not last. Before a year was out, Lord Delaware's health failed and he returned to England to die. Sir Thomas Dale, the high marshal, was appointed acting governor. Delaware left in March, and Dale did not arrive till May. During these months the unruly elements again made trouble. To preserve the colony, Dale was forced to use the severe and often cruel punishments of English martial law.

Francis West went home one evening with a scowl on his usually pleasant face. " 'Tis out of all reason!" he stormed to his wife. "Sir Thomas wishes to tie up the hands of all. A murrain take him!"

"Not so loud, Frank," cautioned Mary. "What's amiss?"

"Sir Thomas has ordered that all who are caught playing at bowls be punished with lashes."

"An o'er sensible command," interposed Master John Rolfe, who made his home with the Wests.

"Sensible!" retorted West. "By what right does he limit the amusement of free men? A game of bowls after the day's work's done but gives a man an appetite for supper."

"Mayhap so," quietly answered Rolfe, "but the noise of bowling is heard at all hours. 'Tis unseemly for God-fearing men to be idling through the hours meant for work. The high marshal has acted wisely."

"Sh-h, Frank!" whispered Madame West. "Say naught to ruffle the poor gentleman. The death of his wife and infant daughter is enow to make him grumpy. 'Tis no wonder he has no pleasure save with religion and tobacco."

Master Rolfe's great fondness for tobacco occasioned much talk.

"Hast heard that Master Rolfe is planting Indian tobacco in the same patch with plants he raised from seed he brought from Bermuda?" said Powell to Martin. "He hopes to take the bite out of the native weed and yet keep a sturdy plant."

"Virginia has many interesting plants," said another. "My Lord la Warre's physician, Dr. Lawrence Bohun, who spent his time here experimenting with the curative powers of plants and herbs, took pecone roots back with him. The Indians dry it and pound it till it turns to red powder. Dr. Bohun found 'twas good for swelling and aching joints."

"Mayhap Captain Smith was right," said Martin, "in holding to the opinion we should make use of commodities found growing on the land, and forget the dream of gold. Look at those mulberry trees! An we could obtain silk worms, we might build a thriving industry."

It was another dark summer for Jamestown. Sir Thomas lacked Lord Delaware's tact and had to use extreme punishment to keep control. Late in the summer Sir Thomas Gates, with an additional three hundred settlers, arrived. He and Dale decided to carry out a plan Dale had cherished for a long time. Because the low, marshy situation of Jamestown was so unhealthy, Dale wished to found a new city on a piece of ground up the river where great bends had made a high plateau of about seven acres. It could be easily defended by building a palisade and digging a moat across the very narrow peninsula connecting it with the mainland.

On account of this easy method of defense, and because its greater distance from the mouth of the river rendered it less likely to be attacked by the Spaniards, most of the families moved to Henricus with Dale. Sir Thomas Gates remained at Jamestown with a garrison of men.

"How are you prospering in your new home?" one of his

men, who had come to Jamestown on an errand, was asked. "Are any left, or are you all main fond o' him?"

"Marry, we are. We are building brick houses and can now rival Jamestown."

" 'Tis food for mirth how you fellows love the watchdog. I am greatly rejoiced to have him leave Jamestown, so evil treated were we."

" 'Tis true his dealings were hard," said John Laydon. "But I mind me he was the man who did away with the common store. 'Twas hard to be ever working and yet be able to lay by naught. Now, with three acres of my own, mayhap I can support a growing family."

"They tell me you have another daughter," said George Percy.

"Aye, Master Percy, and the goodwife calls her Alice. We live at Kecoughtan now, and ere long I hope to be so fixed that we'll ne'er again sigh for England."

"Belike he did us a favor in that case," said Captain Martin. "But there be many who will ne'er forget the foul wrongs he inflicted on us."

"Tut, tut, Master Martin!" said another stranger. "You misjudge Sir Thomas. He is a man of great knowledge in divinity, which is rare in a martial man."

"I cry your pardon, Master Whitaker," said Martin hastily. "It had 'scaped me you are in charge of Sir Thomas's church."

"Is Sir Thomas doing aught for the conversion of the Indians?" asked Master Percy of Master Whitaker.

"Is't true Sir Thomas has sent Captain Argall up the Potomac after corn?" another asked.

The talk now became general and the crowd soon scattered, for the colonists who had left Jamestown had to return home before nightfall.

No one could know it at the time, but the wind blowing softly up the James was filling the sails of a little vessel bringing the little Indian princess, who had not seen Jamestown for more than three years.

CHAPTER XIV

A Captive Comes to Jamestown

Captain Samuel Argall's ship, the *Treasurer,* rode at anchor near the point where the Potomac River empties into the Chesapeake Bay. Only a few men were in sight, and they were idly throwing dice on the deck. Soon a little boat that had been hidden in the brush on the shore was pushed out into the water and approached the ship.

In a few minutes Sam Collier was on deck and reporting at once to Captain Argall: "While scouting through yon woods on the south bank of the river, sir, I chanced to hear someone cleaving fuel. I stole near and, peeping through the bushes, caught sight on Henry Spelman."

"Dost mean the boy Pocahontas saved the last time we went to Weromocomoco?" interrupted Captain Martin.

"Didst hear aught of the princess?" demanded Argall almost in the same breath.

" 'Twas the very same Henry Spelman. I asked him anent the princess, and he told me she was with her cousin, Chief Japazaws. Then he asked me not to speak on't, since she does not wish her father to discover her."

"Mayhap the little maid will persuade Japazaws to sell us corn. She was ever ready to aid us," said Nathaniel Causy.

Just after sundown the little boat again left the ship. In it were Argall and Captain John Martin. They kept silent till they were out of sight of the ship. "Dost feel sure you'll sense the place where we are to meet Japazaws?" asked Martin.

"Marry, I will. So Japazaws finds the place, my scheme will succeed."

"Does anyone know of the purport of our errand?"

"Nay, nay. Collier is the only one who knows we have left the ship. He knows naught save that I wish to speak to Japazaws this even."

"Art sure Japazaws is friendly enow to the English to aid us?"

"Tut, tut, man! Why so uncertain?" said Argall testily. "When Captain Smith was on his voyage up the Chesapeake, Japazaws was so impressed he wished to worship the white men. Now he so loves our trinkets that he would betray his own father to get them. The plan cannot fail, and it will do much to make peace with Powhatan."

They turned into a cove and, after getting out, tied up the boat. Just as they completed that job, they were aware of an Indian standing behind them. "Is't Japazaws?" asked Argall in a very friendly tone, at the same time handing a necklace of beads to the silent figure.

The Indian grunted assent and, after placing the necklace around his neck, silently seated himself on a log. The two white men sat down also. Argall unwrapped a bundle he was carrying and took from it a bright copper kettle. Japazaws reached out his hand eagerly, but Argall kept the kettle out of reach. Then, looking the Indian steadily in the eye, he explained his plot. Japazaws listened attentively, occasionally giving a grunt of amazement. Argall ceased speaking. Then he dropped his voice to a whisper. "Wouldst like to earn the kettle, Japazaws?"

"Princess no do what I say," replied Japazaws sulkily, but keeping his eyes on the kettle.

"Your squaw must needs make her," said Argall. "Once the princess is on the ship, I will do the rest."

"Ugh!" exclaimed Japazaws delightedly. "Beat squaw, beat her."

"Yea," chimed in Martin, "beat her and I'll trow she'll find a way to bring the princess with her."

Early the next morning Argall ordered the ship to sail up

the river, explaining this sudden move by telling the crew he had made arrangements to take on corn. They passed the cove and went on till they reached a village on the south shore of the river. The white men were gladly welcomed and Indian boys at once began to carry great baskets of corn onto the ship. After this was completed, Japazaws, followed by two Indian women, came on board.

There was a murmur of astonishment as some of the men recognized Pocahontas. It was nearly three years since any of the white men had seen her. In that time she had changed from a shy, timid child to a very reserved, dignified young woman. She had not grown any taller, but her manner so impressed the men that they removed their caps. She acknowledged the salute gravely, but showed plainly she did not wish to say anything to her old acquaintances.

Japazaws' squaw was full of curiosity and kept running about peeping into everything while asking her husband questions. Japazaws informed Argall in a loud whisper that she wished to see the kettle. Argall ordered supper to be served. The squaw continued to jabber. In order to attract Argall's attention to her requests, Japazaws commenced to trample on Argall's toes.

As soon as the meal was ended, Pocahontas asked to be taken ashore. Then Argall curtly informed her she was to go to Jamestown with him. The girl looked at him in silent astonishment and Japazaws and his squaw commenced to howl.

Henry Spelman, who had come aboard with Pocahontas, sprang forward angrily. "By all the saints, she shall not go an she objects!"

"You stupid oaf!" sneered Argall. "One more word and you'll balk yourself of going with her. So you do not wish a cold bath, you'll hold your tongue."

Pocahontas had recovered from her astonishment and her eyes were shining with anger. "You'll not dare to touch me," she said courageously. "Powhatan and Captain Smith will punish you."

"Let the old Indian do his worst," laughed Argall, "and

Captain Smith has been dead so long e'en his bones are lost."

The girl turned swiftly away, her eyes full of tears and her lips quivering.

"Nay, Argall," said Nathaniel Causy warmly, " 'tis not right to capture the maid in this fashion."

"She has been our good friend in the past," urged another. "It ill fits us to use her badly now."

"Belike it will rouse Powhatan against us once more," added Causy.

"I refuse to be said in such fashion by any man!" replied Argall angrily. "The emprise is in my hands. As for rousing Powhatan, 'tis for the purpose of making peace with him that I am taking his daughter. He'll not dare to hurt us so long as she is among us. Here you, Japazaws, stop that racket and take that bawling hag away. Here's your kettle. Now go."

As the ship started back down the river, Master Causy approached the motionless figure of the girl. "Do not take it to heart too sorely," he said kindly. "No harm will come to you, and when we reach Jamestown, I'll see you are taken to Mistress Pierce. She and little Jane will care for you till we can send you back to your own people."

The girl smiled at him gratefully but did not speak. For the next two days she sat on deck gazing helplessly at the water, not making a sound.

There was great excitement when Argall and his well known prisoner appeared at Jamestown. Many, especially those who had known Pocahontas formerly, were indignant at the way she had been treated and strongly urged sending her back to her father. Others, including Sir Thomas Gates, were impressed with Argall's scheme for bringing Powhatan to terms so easily and readily agreed to keep the girl till the old Indian could be heard from. A message was sent to Powhatan telling him of the capture of his daughter and saying that if he would release some Englishmen he had in captivity and restore tools and swords that had been stolen, Pocahontas would be sent back to him; otherwise, she would be held as a prisoner.

Because Henricus was more easily defended than Jamestown and the women of the colony were living there, it was decided to send Pocahontas there under the guardianship of Sir Thomas Dale. Mistress Pierce readily consented to take the frightened, sobbing girl into her home. The good woman was touched by the girl's plight and threw her motherly arms around her. "Alackaday, lassie," she murmured caressingly, "this will never do. Come now, dry your eyes and try to be happy. Mother Pierce will take care of you. Here, Jane, take the princess out in the yard and show her the young fig trees your father has planted."

As the fair-haired English girl and the brunette Virginian went out together, they little thought that in the years to come their lives and the lives of their children would be closely inter-twined through the life of the man each one was to marry.

"Mary, Maid Mary mine," called Francis West, running to his comely wife, as he always did when he had news, "the princess has come to town and is to stay with your gossip, Mistress Pierce."

"My, my!" she replied excitedly. "What will happen next? The Spanish spies and that traitorous Englishman taken prisoner last month, and now the Indian princess. Truly, our little colony is gathering a motley crowd. I'll run over to see Mistress Pierce for a bit and then come back to tell you all about it."

For three months nothing was heard from Powhatan. Then he sent, by way of ransom, seven Englishmen, three muskets and a canoe of corn. Gates laughed dryly as he spoke to the messenger. "Tell Powhatan his daughter shall be well used. But we cannot believe the rest of our arms were either lost or stolen from him, and till he sends them, we will keep his daughter." Nothing more was heard from Powhatan, so Pocahontas remained with the English through the winter.

As time passed, she became contented in her new surroundings. She always had a fondness for the colonists, and now that she lived among them, she soon adjusted herself to their ways.

" 'Tis ever a wonder to me," Mistress Pierce confided to

Madame West, "how that Indian girl learns. When she came, she knew naught. Now she can redd up the house as well as Jane can. She is learning to embroider, as well. Master Rolfe has given her a length of that red silk mochado that came in his last shipment from home, and she plans to ornament a robe for herself."

"Is she not fond o' tricking herself out in colors?" laughed Madame West.

"Certes; an I do not watch her, she would don her Sunday kirtle on weekdays. 'Tis a wonder she did not 'spute me when I took away her savage clothes, but she seemed pleased on't."

"Master Rolfe seems much interested in her," continued Madame West. " 'Twas only last night he brought Master Whitaker home to supper, and they spent much time discussing the possibilities of her conversion. Frank says Sir Thomas is so anxious for her instruction that he has asked Master Whitaker to take her to Rock Hall so he can catechize her daily. He finds her sadly ignorant, though she can call to mind what good Master Hunt used to teach her. They say Captain Smith was teaching her to read. Does she ever talk anent the captain?"

"Nay. I asked her once anent the time she saved his life, but she seemed not to wish to talk on't. She is so shy that I like not to press her."

"Captain Powell says she was o'er fond o' Captain Smith. Dost think she is like to go back to her father and marry an Indian brave?" Madame West lowered her voice discreetly and whispered, " 'Tis my rede she is taking notice o' one that is nearer than the Pamunkey, and that he thinks o' her is plain."

"Sh-h-h," Mistress Pierce murmured. "I must mind you she is a savage for all she is a princess, and Christian men are forbidden to marry strange wives."

"Belike she becomes a Christian. What wouldst say then?"

Discreet Miss Pierce changed the subject of the conversation and then did not repeat it. So the shy Indian girl and the honest young English gentleman were not aware that several pairs of sharp eyes were noticing the interest they took in each other.

CHAPTER XV

Wedding Bells

For some weeks Master John Rolfe had been distraught. His endeavor always had been to live a well ordered, God-fearing life, doing each day what seemed to be his duty, and not yielding to any physical temptations or disorders that might turn him from his planned path. Now he was having difficulty in controlling his thoughts, and it irked him.

It was a mild day in early spring. He had taken his three servants out to where he had cleared ground the previous fall. It was a gentle, southeasterly slope, catching the full force of the morning sun. He had set the boys to burning off the undergrowth, and it was his plan to spend the day there with them, having them drag the burning embers back and forth over the cleared space so as to destroy seeds as well as larger growths. He was intensely interested in the experiments he had been making during the past two years with tobacco. By crossing the native Indian weed with plants he had raised from Spanish seed brought from the Bermudas, he had developed a strain that was proving popular in England. His agent had written that the last shipment had been in fine shape when it arrived, due to a new method he had used for curing the leaves the previous year. He had added that there would be a demand for all Rolfe could send this year. Rolfe was taking special care in preparing this ground on which he planned to scatter the tiny seeds. Perhaps if he burned off all the weeds on this protected patch and then covered the seeds with canvas so the wind could not blow other seeds there, he could protect the tender plants. He hoped to grow enough to be able to give some to his neighbors, so they could share his prosperity.

Since all was going well, why should he feel oppressed with a feeling of uncertainty? For once, physical toil did not bring him the ease he was seeking. The boys understood what he wanted them to do and were making a game of their task, so Master Rolfe sat down on a log and gave himself up to his thoughts. He was sure he had not been prompted solely by the drift of the times when he had joined the band of settlers who were going to Virginia. It had not proved to be the glowing adventure they had pictured before they embarked. First there was the hurricane, and then the shipwreck. That had not proved too disastrous, for God had saved the lives of all and they were able to live comfortably that winter on the tropical island. But then had come the birth and death of his little daughter, and later his wife, too, had died. That had ended his dream of founding a Christian home in this new land. Conditions could not have been worse when they finally reached Jamestown, with the people starving and the town in ruins. Then the providential arrival of Lord Delaware had saved the colony.

Conditions were so different from what he had been led to expect that he had toyed with the idea of returning to England, since he had paid his own passage and was not beholden to the London Company. But even if conditions were different, his ideals had not changed. His main reason for coming to Virginia had been to aid in spreading Christianity among the Indians through the establishment of an English colony. He was not tempted by the idea of amassing riches, as were many of the adventurers. Perhaps it was because the work of spreading Christianity was going so slowly that he was feeling discontented. He and Sir Thomas Dale and Master Whitaker talked of it constantly. Master Whitaker prayed fervently at every service for a way to be opened to them. Now, after all these years, the only native who was showing any interest in Christianity was the Indian maiden Pocahontas. He stirred uneasily as he realized he had been trying all morning to keep her out of his mind. It seemed that no matter when he attempted to give himself up to meditation, his thoughts worked around to this girl. Why should an educated English gentleman be thinking constantly of a girl ten years his junior, and a savage, as well? An involuntary smile caused his face to light up. Jane Pierce and Master Whitaker's daughter were attractive, but they did not hold his attention as the Indian girl did. She was shy and diffident, but as she had learned and adopted more English ways and customs, she had developed a pleasing dignity the two younger girls lacked. The Scriptures were right when they said that it was not good for man to dwell alone.

He suddenly stood up, astonished at his own thoughts. Why should a Christian man be thinking in this way of a heathen, for that was what Pocahontas was, for all her gentle, sweet ways. The Scriptures also forbade the Israelites to marry strangers. But on the other hand, if, by marrying an unbeliever, he could lead her to accept Christianity, would he not be furthering the Kingdom? As he paced up and down under the giant trees, he forced himself for the first time to face the question. He did desire the girl, but at the same time he was resolved not to let this natural feeling overcome his high ideals. He sat down abruptly with his head in his hands as his thoughts seemed to spin in an endless circle. It was more than he could handle alone. Perhaps it would be best to leave the boys to their own devices and go to Rock Hall to consult with Master Whitaker.

At the sight of Rolfe, the gentle clergyman recognized a soul in distress and he led the young man away from the house to where they could talk privately.

Rolfe needed no encouragement. "I am enthralled in so intricate a labyrinth of my own thoughts, it wearies me to endeavor to unwind myself!" he burst out.

"Proceed, my son," said Whitaker quietly.

"I protest I am not being led by the unbridled desire of a carnal affection. My hope is for the good of this plantation, the honor of our country, the glory of God, my own salvation and the converting to the true knowledge of God and Jesus Christ of an unbelieving creature."

"Yes?" murmured the clergyman. He did not understand the intense emotion of his visitor, but thought it best to let him unburden himself in his own way.

"My thoughts have been such that I feared Satan, who plans for man's destruction, was making a diabolical assault on me. I have fasted. I have prayed. Just today I seem to be finding the light." The young man was nervously clasping and unclasping his hands. "For weeks I have not allowed myself to see her, hoping it would breed forgetfulness, but it has not."

Master Whitaker asked his first question. "Who is she, my son?"

Rolfe almost choked as he replied, "The Indian maiden."

"Pocahontas?" exclaimed Master Whitaker in stunned surprise.

Rolfe nodded. "Mayhap an I should marry her, I could aid in her conversion. I could not feel justified in seeking my own welfare did I not feel I was called by the Spirit of God."

"The maiden is near to the Kingdom," said Whitaker. "An she returns to her father and marries a heathen, it might lead to her soul's destruction. Perhaps God has called you to complete this holy work, especially," he added with a gentle smile, "as your heart is leading you."

Rolfe removed his cap and bowed his head as if in prayer. "I will never cease," he said reverently, "God helping me, till I have accomplished and brought to perfection this holy work. I will daily pray God to bless me and her as I strive for her eternal happiness."

But before Rolfe could take steps to further his romance, other matters claimed his attention. Sir Thomas Gates had returned to England, leaving Sir Thomas Dale as deputy governor. Dale decided they could wait no longer on Powhatan, and that it would be best to take Pocahontas to Weromocomoco and there negotiate her return. Taking the girl with them, a hundred and fifty men set out on a vessel for the York River. To the surprise of all, Pocahontas seemed loath to leave the settlement and at the last clung so tearfully to Mistress Pierce and Mistress Whitaker that the good women begged Sir Thomas to leave the girl behind. But the high marshal had made his plans and, despite the tears of the women, took Pocahontas with him.

In three days they reached Weromocomoco, but found that the emperor was not there. After a skirmish with the Indians, who seemed unfriendly, they pushed on to Machit. The Indians there also seemed unfriendly, but Dale soon quieted the rising disturbance and the Indians agreed to keep peace until Powhatan could be heard from.

"Master Rolfe," said Sir Thomas, "you and Master Sparkes are to accompany these lads in search of Powhatan. Tell him an he does not fulfil my orders, I'll burn every house on this river and not leave a fish weir nor canoe in any creek."

After the searchers left, a tall young warrior presented himself to Captain Powell. "Dost mind who I am?" he asked.

"Nantauquas!" exclaimed Powell. "How glad the princess will be."

"Is she well? Word came she was ailing and unhappy."

"Nay, nay, lad. Come see for yourself."

Pocahontas gave a glad cry of welcome when she saw her brother, and threw her arms about him. "Dost love me yet, Nantauquas?" she asked eagerly. "If Powhatan loved me, he would not value me less than swords and axes. I am not coming back to live with him, but shall stay with the English, who love me."

Powell left them together and went back to the other men. He found them in the greatest excitement, all talking at once. "What's toward now?" he asked Causy.

" 'Tis a letter Master Rolfe left to be given to Sir Thomas. Master Rolfe wishes to marry Pocahontas."

"What says Sir Thomas?"

"He has said naught yet. Poor Master Rolfe plainly loves the maiden; but she belongs to a cursed generation, and his love has caused a war in his meditations. Her desire to be instructed in the knowledge of God's Word has roused the question whether 'tis not his duty to marry and convert this unbelieving creature."

When Rolfe and Sparkes returned from their fruitless quest, Dale had decided the important question. He told Rolfe the marriage could take place at once provided Pocahontas would consent to be baptised. Nantauquas promised to gain the consent of his father. The party returned to Jamestown immediately, and all the women in the colony at once began preparations for the wedding.

Pocahontas took the excitement quietly, but seemed disturbed when they told her she must choose a Christian name for herself. She turned to Master Whitaker for counsel, and he proposed that she call herself Rebecca. The following Sunday, in the little frame church at Jamestown, Pocahontas was baptised by Master Richard Buck. On account of her position as the emperor's daughter, she was allowed to assume the title of Lady Rebecca. Sir Thomas and Master Rolfe joined in the service with fervor.

The next week the wedding took place, and there never was a gayer one. Pocahontas had won the hearts of the English, and they vied with each other to show her honor. Before daylight Sam Collier and Henry Spelman crossed to the mainland and brought back great branches of dogwood to decorate the chancel of the church.

Powhatan, who had vowed never to trust himself within the bounds of an English town, refused to attend, but sent his brother to give the bride away. Nantauquas and a sister also attended. They brought with them for Pocahontas a tiny, intricately woven basket. When she looked into it, she gave her accustomed cry of delight. "My earrings! My earrings!" she exclaimed. "See!"—as she held them out to Mistress Pierce, who came to see what was afoot. In the girl's hand were two tiny gleaming-white pairs of mussel shells.

"They came many years ago from waters far across the mountains," explained Nantauquas. "My father wishes my sister to have them. Only a great chief's daughter may wear them."

"Come, lassie," said Mistress Pierce, " 'tis time to don your wedding garment." She helped the girl slip over her head a tunic of fine white muslin. Over that she wore the beautiful robe of silk machado she had embroidered herself. A glittering band across her forehead helped to hold the veil in place, and in her ears were the earrings.

"Frank," called Madame West, "come do on your Sunday doublet."

"Tut, tut, 'tis not becoming in a military man to think o'er much o' clothes," replied that gentleman, but at the same time preparing to obey his wife's wishes. "Heyday, madam, *you* are still in your workaday clothes."

"I've been so put about trying to get Master Rolfe ready! The good gentleman wished to have some time for prayer and gave me no rest till he was dressed. I thought all was ready, but at the last minute he wished the ruffles in the sleeve of his doublet changed, and he stood me down that the rosettes on his shoes were not sewed on aright. Now I'll into my cramoisie satin kirtle, that I've not put on since I came to Virginia. Frank, be sure to brush your beard, and put the civet on't."

An hour later Master Buck had read the words of the beautiful English service that made John Rolfe and Pocahontas man and wife. Just at the close of the service, as the bride and groom stood with bowed heads and clasped hands, a shaft of sunlight came through the church window and cast a bright ray over the dark hair of the Indian girl. It formed a halo around her head and made her appear, in very truth, the angel of peace between the two races then living in Virginia.

This alliance did for many years prove to be a blessing of peace. The tribe of the Chickahominies at once concluded a treaty by which they became subjects of the English king, and in token of this new arrangement, a brass tablet having upon it the words of the treaty was nailed to a tree on the bank of the river.

CHAPTER XVI

Virginia Loses Her Princess

Pocahontas soon learned to preside over her home with the grace of an English lady. Her love for her own people never wavered, but the English life and customs suited her better. Owing to her father's thoughtfulness and care, she was surrounded by Indian servants. And thanks to Mistress Pierce and Mistress Whitaker, she was an accomplished housekeeper.

"Rebecca," said Master Rolfe one day, for he always used and insisted on others using her Christian name, "has Rawhunt been here of late? 'Tis about time he was bringing a fresh supply of corn."

"I expect him within a se'ennight, Master Rolfe," she replied in her soft, lisping voice. "He doth but wait till the fresh ears are large enow to use. When they come, we must ask Master Whitaker over from Rock Hall. 'Tis one of the few things he craves."

"How know you that, Rebecca?" Rolfe asked in surprise.

"I heard Mistress Whitaker say so, and 'tis easy to remember the likes of one you love."

Rolfe looked at her quizzically. In spite of his great affection for her, he had hesitated to ask her to marry him, on account of religious scruples. Now he found himself continually amazed at the hold religion had on her thoughts and actions. He repeated the remark to Sir Thomas.

"Master Rolfe," commented that gentleman feelingly, "were it only for the sake of winning this one precious soul, I would not consider my time in Virginia lost."

114

The next year was an uneventful one for the princess. Now that the colonists no longer had to fear an Indian attack, affairs in the plantation were gradually becoming settled on a firmer basis. The gold fever had about passed. Instead, various settlers were trying out different experiments in an effort to find profitable commodities for export. Glass manufacturing was still interesting a few, and others were urging the importation of silkworms. But it was Master Rolfe who had hit upon the crop that was to prove the economic foundation of the colony. He was now giving all his time to the cultivation of tobacco, which was rapidly becoming profitable. Indeed, he had given the whole neighborhood the name Varina, for he insisted that the tobacco raised in that locality was as fine-flavored as the Spanish variety of that name. Other colonists were also growing tobacco and, as a result, were settling on plantations up and down the James River. With the exception of a proportion of the crop that had to be paid to the Company's treasurer, each man kept what he made.

"Oh, Mistress Pierce!" exclaimed Madame West one day, running excitedly into her friend's house, "hast heard the great news? There is a little son born to Master and Mistress Rolfe."

"What might his name be?" asked Mistress Pierce.

"He is to be called Thomas after Sir Thomas Dale, who is to stand as his godfather when Master Whitaker christens him this next Sunday. Our little Indian girl is still showing herself to be a good Christian."

But the interest aroused by the arrival of Thomas Rolfe was not to be compared with the excitement that took possession of every man, woman and child when it became known that Sir Thomas Dale was returning to England for a visit and Master Rolfe and Pocahontas were accompanying him. "They do say," said Master West in giving an account to his wife of what he had heard, "that Sir Thomas is to take a dozen Indians with him."

"Will he take Rawhunt?" asked Madame West. "Methinks Master Will Shakespeare would like to steal the poor misshapen body for a villain in one of his plays. He would make a likely one."

"I know not about Rawhunt, but Tomocomo is to go. Powhatan has given him a stick, and on it he is to put a notch for every white man he sees in England. The old chief wishes to number our forces."

Madame West laughed gaily. "Tomocomo will wear out his stick or ever he leaves Plymouth, so we need not fear the numbering. Frank, you must write your sister-in-law, Lady la Warre, and ask her to show Pocahontas some courtesy. She'll find no better-mannered lady in all England than our Lady Rebecca, I'll warrant."

As always with each new experience, Pocahontas took delight in the voyage to England. It was not as long as it had been ten years previously, for they now used the route charted by Captain Argall, which took them due east to the Azores, instead of going the longer way around, through the West Indies and the Canary Islands. One tragic happening marred the pleasure of the trip. After having held them as prisoners at Jamestown for three years, Sir Thomas was taking back to England the Spanish spies and their traitorous English accomplice, Francis Lymbry. Almost in sight of England, Sir Thomas decided to hang Lymbry. Rolfe decided to tell Pocahontas of the plan rather than risk her hearing of it suddenly. She looked at him in wide-eyed horror. "No, no, 'tis not Christian to do so! I'll beg for his life from Sir Thomas."

In spite of Rolfe's protest, she went directly to Dale's quarters. At first sight of his visitor, Sir Thomas looked pleased, but when he heard her request, his face darkened. "The law requires traitors to be punished by death," he said sternly.

"Christian law says different," she pleaded. "Scripture says we should show mercy to our enemies."

"Master Whitaker must not have taught you all the Scriptures. Do you not mind how God commanded the Israelites to slay their enemies till not one was left alive?"

"But the Sermon on the Mount——" she began timidly. Sir Thomas brought his hand heavily down on the table. "Have done, madam. I know my duty." Pocahontas ran sobbing back to her cabin and stayed there for the rest of the voyage.

Sir Thomas spoke to Master Rolfe about it, and he defended his wife. "Poor little maid! She has seen o'er much o' bloodshed, and her heart is tender and loving to all. She thinks her people are cruel because they are heathen, and she has come to believe Christians show mercy."

"Bah!" replied Sir Thomas. "She has been trained by women and clergymen. She must learn that English martial law punishes traitors."

It was June, 1616, when Sir Thomas Dale and his party reached England. The Indians, and especially Pocahontas, aroused great excitement. After a few days in Plymouth they were planning to go to London, but an unpleasant circumstance detained them.

"There is some gossip I have to tell you, Master Rolfe," said Sir Thomas, "and it may alter your plan to take your wife to London. I sent the letter Master West writ to his brother, Lord la Warre, and this day I had a reply from my Lady. She says the king is very wroth at your having married the princess without his permission, and 'twill not be wise for His Majesty to see you."

"What might the trouble be?" asked Rolfe in amazement.

"Pocahontas is Powhatan's daughter, and Powhatan is the ruler of Virginia. 'Tis like the kingdom might descend to Pocahontas at Powhatan's death. At her death the kingdom would be vested in your posterity."

" 'Tis like King James to show such petty jealousy," replied Rolfe in disgust.

"Not so loud, man. At any rate, 'twill not be wise to take the Lady Rebecca to London till the king have time to forget his vexation."

Then another letter was received from Lady Delaware. It seemed that Captain John Smith, on hearing of Pocahontas' arrival in England, had written a letter to Queen Anne, recommending the Indian princess to royal favor. He told of the many times she had saved the colony from destruction. He closed the letter by asking that favor be shown her in view of her desert, birth and simplicity. This letter had the desired effect, and Lady Delaware had been asked to present the princess at court. Pocahontas said nothing when she was told of Smith's intervention in her behalf.

" 'Tis strange she shows so little interest," said Sir Thomas. "Dost think she has forgotten Captain Smith?"

"Nay, nay," replied Rolfe. "She ne'er forgets aught, and Captain Smith was kind to her. An she cared for him as his old soldiers say she did, she has not forgot him."

Pocahontas had been in London only a few days when Captain Smith came to see her. She was in the garden alone at the time, and he came upon her there unexpectedly. "Give thee good day, Lady Rebecca," he said, making a profound bow.

She gave a start of surprise and then covered her face with her hands. When she lifted her eyes, he was surprised at the change in them. When he had first come upon her, he had hardly known her. Now she seemed suddenly to have changed back into the shy little girl in the Virginia woods. She looked at him a moment, and when she spoke, her voice took on the little lisp she had almost lost in her association with the English.

"You did promise Powhatan that what was yours should be his. You called him father, being in his land a stranger. Fear you I should call you father here?"

"Nay, nay, my lady," he responded gently. "You are the daughter of an emperor, and 'tis meet you should preserve your dignity."

"You showed no fear to come to Virginia and make all my people, save me, afraid. But you fear in England for me to call you father. I tell you then that I will, and you shall call me child." She looked at him steadily and then whispered, "They did tell me ever you were dead, and I knew no other till I came to Plymouth."

"Nay, my Princess. My life has been many times in danger, but God, in His great goodness, has saved me alive. Now I must leave you. I sail soon from England, and I know not that I shall e'er see you again. God bless you!" And then, in answer to the unspoken request in her eyes, he whispered gently, "God bless you, little maid!"

"Good-by, my Captain," she responded brightly, extending her hand. He knelt and kissed it and the next moment was gone.

Pocahontas spent a gay winter in England. She was presented at court, and after the queen had complimented her, she became the fashion. The Bishop of London invited her to dinner. She attended balls and masques and even went to the theater to see Master Shakespeare's new play *The Tempest*, which was based on the wreck of the *Sea Venture* in the Bermuda Islands. It was whispered that Calaban was drawn from the accounts Master Shakespeare had heard of Rawhunt, the deformed Indian. It was also thought that Miranda was meant for Pocahontas, but the princess always denied that idea. She had her portrait painted twice. In one she is dressed as an English lady, with a high lace collar and ostrich-feather fan. In the other she is dressed as a Virginian. She is wearing a crimson-velvet tunic trimmed in cut steel. A string of pearls is around her neck. Her straight black hair is parted in the middle and pushed behind her ears, in which are the shell earrings. Her little son is standing by her side, within the crook of her right arm. When the Duke of Northumberland, Master George Percy's brother, saw the earrings, he asked the honor of having them set in silver for her.

Early in February, Pocahontas developed a bad cough. The doctors tried in vain to stop it. They told Master Rolfe that the damp winter had been too hard on her and advised him to take her back to Virginia. The party started immediately, but when it arrived at Gravesend, the princess became so ill it was necessary to postpone the journey. In spite of the best care that could be given, she sank rapidly.

"Master Rolfe," she whispered one day, "bring me my boy. Poor little man!"—as she caressed him—"'tis ill to lose your mother so young. Wilt promise me something, Master Rolfe?"

"Yea, Rebecca."

"I wish my boy to be brought up among the white men, but teach him to love my people." Her eyes filled as she looked at the smiling child in her arms. "Never let him forget that his mother loved him very tenderly."

"Nay, Rebecca, you must not talk so. You will mend soon. The boy and I need you."

"Yea, but it is not to be. I would fain see Virginia once more," she murmured dreamily. "Dost promise what I ask, Master Rolfe?"

"Yea, Rebecca," he answered solemnly.

It was the last of March when she died, just as the violets and dogwood were beginning to bloom in Virginia. She was buried in the church at Gravesend, and her name was registered as Rebecca Rolfe. But today she lives in the hearts of Americans as Pocahontas, the little Indian princess.